2

TEST REPORTS

THE ROUTER

AND

FURNITURE & CABINETMAKING

TEST REPORTS

THE ROUTER
AND
FURNITURE & CABINETMAKING

GUILD OF MASTER CRAFTSMAN PUBLICATIONS LTD

This collection first published 1998 by
Guild of Master Craftsman Publications Ltd,
Castle Place, 166 High Street, Lewes, East Sussex BN7 1XU

© GMC Publications 1998

ISBN 1 86108 102 2

Printed and bound by Kyodo Printing (Singapore) under the supervision
of MRM Graphics, Winslow, Buckinghamshire, UK

Front cover photograph by Anthony Bailey

IMPORTANT INFORMATION FOR READERS

This book consists of test reports published between November 1996 and May 1998. The reports are reproduced as they were originally published.

This means that prices may have changed since first publication, and for this reason a comprehensive, up-to-date list of addresses and phone numbers is included under 'Contact Addresses', on pages 116-118.

Readers are strongly advised to contact the relevant supplier for the latest information on prices, models, availability, etc.

CONTENTS

INTRODUCTION

Of all the craft pursuits, woodworking requires the greatest investment in equipment – and few woodworkers are faced with quite the range of tools and machines that the furniture-maker considers essential. This means that a sound knowledge of currently-available equipment is important if costly mistakes are to be avoided.

The other side of the coin is that fresh possibilities are presented by new developments – makers might find laminating and veneering work can be cost-effective for them on learning of a new vacuum press, for example.

So there are two good excuses for doing something that all woodworkers secretly enjoy – reading about tools and machines.

From its first issue, *Furniture & Cabinetmaking* magazine broke new ground by instituting a programme of real-world tests of woodworking equipment, carried out by experienced furniture-makers with practical knowledge of working with machines. This meant that for the first time, prospective buyers had access to unbiased information about the actual usability of a machine in situations similar to their own – not just a description and list of specifications.

Since then this formula has been successfully applied to equipment as diverse as combination woodworking machines and biscuit jointers, dimension saws and cordless drills – in fact, almost everything that is needed when making furniture.

It's not surprising that *F&C*'s sister magazine, *The Router*, follows the same principle of real-world, hands-on testing; its Editor is Alan Goodsell who, as *F&C*'s Technical Editor, was responsible for most of its test reports.

The field of routers, cutters and accessories is easily the fastest-growing in woodworking, with new developments emerging all the time as new ways of exploiting this versatile power tool are discovered – so here it is even more important to keep in touch.

This book brings together the most useful tests so far published in these two magazines, aiming to provide a practical resource of advice and information to save the woodworker time, money and frustration.

I think it makes a pretty good read as well.

Paul Richardson
Editor, *Furniture & Cabinetmaking*

F&C Editor **Paul Richardson** assesses the DW705 large capacity compound mitre saw from DeWalt

PIHOTOGRAPHY BY ANTHONY BAILEY

All the angles

● **Price: £587.50 including VAT Contact: DeWalt on 01753 567055**

CHOP, OR MITRE, saws are still a bit of a novelty in the UK. In the USA these portable machines are so popular that a whole industry has grown up supplying accessories such as wheeled stands, length stops and so on. This is largely due to the predominance of timber as a primary building material for houses, although the American enthusiasm for dedicated power tools must also play a part.

Yet another saw?

So are these saws useful to the furniture maker? Certainly those of us who spend time on site fitting kitchens, bedrooms and so on have to mitre cornice mouldings away

from the comfort of the workshop, and we all get roped into ad hoc cutting sometimes.

In the workshop we generally have a choice of machine on which to crosscut — radial arm saw, tilt arbor sawbench — so perhaps yet another option is unnecessary. Having said that, very little general crosscutting exceeds 200mm, so a chop saw could free up the larger machines. For quick mitring — especially bevel cuts — something like the DW705 is also quicker to set up — and re-set to zero — than a radial arm saw.

Construction

This machine is constructed largely from cast aluminium, heavily webbed under the beds to maintain flatness. The fences are fitted to the main bed and the left-hand fence has a tall extension which slides laterally to allow for bevel cutting.

Also mounted on the main bed is the turntable, again a heavy alloy casting. This pivots freely when the twist-to-lock knob is released, and locates positively, with a sprung latch, into détente positions at the commonly used angles. Two points are provided for fitting the optional work-clamp, seen in the photograph.

At the rear of the bed is the pivot for adjusting the bevel angle — no détentes here apart from zero — and a large toggle lever to lock.

The primary pivot, allowing the motor, blade and guard assembly to swing down, has substantial bearings with no discernible play, and is

sprung to return to the raised position at rest. A simple draw pin locks the assembly down for carrying by the moulded handle on top of the motor.

In use

A crosscut and mitre saw lives or dies by its repeatable accuracy. Adjustability is all very well, but as many radial arm saw owners will testify, too much can be a curse.

While this machine was on test I had to produce a dozen large mitred frames for a textiles exhibit, and every one was consistent. The pre-set détentes are nicely accurate, and the feel of the numerous moving parts is good. Accuracy is helped by the excellent standard-equipment blade, a laser-cut 32-tooth TCT example, and the over-specified 1500W motor. The brush motor fitted is typically noisy though, kicking in with a vengeance quite unlike that of the induction type found on radial arm saws.

Conclusion

Easy to set up, portable, powerful — this is a tool which has been designed to earn its keep and perform well under any conditions. In the relatively gentle hands of a furniture maker I would expect it to last a very long time. The individual must decide whether a chop saw would suit their way of working, but if the answer is yes then the DeWalt will do the job, and keep doing it.

SPECIFICATIONS

Voltage	110/230
Motor power	1500W
Blade	TCT, 32-tooth 305mm
No load speed	3,800rpm
Weight	17.2kg
Mitre	−48° to 48°
Bevel	−3° to 48°

CAPACITY:

0° mitre:	up to 200mm width up to 90mm height
45° mitre:	up to 140mm width up to 90mm height
45° bevel:	up to 200mm width up to 58mm height

Rexon MS-10RA

Technical Editor **Alan Goodsell** finds a mitre saw that cuts a keen price

ALMOST EVERY power tool manufacturer makes a mitre saw, and most of these machines incorporate a feature designed to make them stand out from the rest.

So how does the Rexon make its mark in mitre saw land? The answer lies in its price — at a trim £199 I believe it is the cheapest 250mm, 10in mitre saw on the market — and I could detect no desperate compromises in the construction of the machine to attain this price.

It has a machined, cast aluminium bed, fence and guard, and the motor housing and saw handle are plastic; a rubberised mounting helps to absorb vibration.

Turntable

The turntable has positive indents on 0°, 15°, 22.5°, 30° and 45° both ways; an extra 60° angle is available on the right. It can be locked in any position in between the stops, and for compound mitres the saw can be tilted to any angle between 0° and 45°.

The turntable's plastic handle is not very rigid and would be the first thing on the saw to break.

The transparent saw guard lifts out of the way when the saw is pulled down; the mechanism for this is external and a little clunky.

Motor

When the safety hand grip is pulled in and the thumb switch is pressed, the 1.7kw motor leaps into life and powers the good quality 250mm, 10in TCT blade. It didn't grumble at cutting 75 x 38mm, 3 x 1 $\frac{1}{2}$in oak (*Quercus sp*) either square or at an angle.

The fence is adjustable to enable it to be set up square to the blade; also to allow a greater capacity. It is on the small side but a larger wooden fence can be fixed to it.

Hold-down clamp

A large-footed hold-down clamp can be fitted either side of the machine, but in certain positions on the right side it fouls the motor. A dust bag is standard and helps cut down workshop dust, and a vacuum extractor can be fitted to the bag's mounting to improve extraction.

A pair of extension bars with a stop are available as extras; not of the best quality, nonetheless they are worth having for the added convenience they provide.

Site and workshop

The convenient carrying handle demonstrates that this saw is aimed at someone who spends a lot of time on site, but it will find a place in the workshop for cutting large mouldings like cornices, for which job setting up a radial arm saw is a pain.

And at £199 inclusive of VAT this tool has to be a bargain.

Contact: Rexon Ltd, 1 The Summit, Barbot Hall Industrial Estate, Maningham Road, Rotherham S61 4RJ, tel 01709 361158, fax 01709 821966. ■

SPECIFICATIONS	
Motor	1700W
Blade	250mm, 10in diameter
Speed	5,000rpm
Capacity:	
At 0° mitre, 0° bevel:	89 x 92mm, 3$\frac{1}{2}$ x 3$\frac{5}{8}$in or
	67 x 164mm, 2$\frac{5}{8}$ x 6$\frac{1}{2}$in
At 45° mitre 0° bevel:	70 x 89mm, 2$\frac{3}{4}$ x 3$\frac{1}{2}$in or
	70 x 105mm, 2$\frac{2}{4}$ x 4in
At 0° mitre 45° bevel:	44 x 130m m, 1$\frac{3}{4}$ x 5in or
	44 x 140mm, 1$\frac{3}{4}$ x 5$\frac{1}{2}$in
At 45° mitre 45° bevel:	44 x 89mm, 1$\frac{3}{4}$ x 3$\frac{1}{2}$in or
	44 x 105mm, 1$\frac{3}{4}$ x 4in
Mitre indents	0°, 15°, 22.5°, 30°, 45° L & R, 60, R only
Table size	Turntable 260mm diameter
	Overall size (L x W x H) 546 x 539 x 486mm
Bevel stop	0° to 45°
RRP	£199 inc. VAT

Sliding Sidekick

F&C Editor **Paul Richardson** gets out of the workshop with Delta's 36-250 sliding compound mitre saw

FACTS AND FIGURES

Motor	1400W
Blade	250mm, 10in 40t TCT
Speed	5000rpm
Capacity:	
Depth at 0° bevel	92mm, 3 $^5/_8$in
Depth at 45° bevel,	51mm, 2in
Width at 0° mitre	305mm, 11 $^1/_2$in
Width at 45° mitre	203mm, 8in
Mitre indents	0°, 22$^1/_2$°, 31.62° and 45° L & R
Bevel stops	0° and 45° L
Weight including stand	24kg, 55lb
Price	£698 inc VAT - check with stockist for best price
Contact	Delta UK, tel 01943 873535, fax 01943 875959

WORKING ON site can be a traumatic experience for a workshop-dwelling cabinetmaker. The prospect of fitting a cornice away from the security of my machinery has me packing half the workshop into the van – on one memorable occasion we took a radial arm saw with a 600mm, 24in cross-cut into a client's house just to cut some worktop edging. Well, there were some tricky angles involved.

Bells and whistles

The new breed of chopsaws, although designed for house-building carpenters in the States, offers a cheaper solution to this kind of irrational fear than psychotherapy can provide. As with the two previous mitre saws tested (pp. 3-4), this example will make mitred cuts from 90° to 45°, both left and right, and bevel cuts from 90° to 45° left, including all compound angle combinations.

The 36-250 offers two additional bells and whistles; the first being an extended cross-cut achieved by mounting the saw on two bars which slide into housings beneath the work table. This gives a capacity of 305mm, 11 $^1/_2$in, more than enough for most site needs. Bell and whistle number two is a folding leg stand and extended work-support. This can be left permanently mounted to the saw even when being moved, as it collapses into a neat package which adds little weight to the saw, which then fits easily into the smallest car boot.

On the face of it, then, the itinerant cabinetmaker's dream – the only thing it won't do is rip, but this rarely requires the precision of a long mitre and is best done with a hand-held circular saw anyway.

Does it measure up to its promise in use? The saw is packed ready-mounted to the stand, so the first job is to extend the legs and work-supports. This takes about 30 seconds. I have to say that first impressions are the worst with the 36-250, as the machine does sway around on the stand – this is the trade-off for light weight and portability, I suppose. The manual explains that an alternative mounting is catered for, using sawn four-by-two carcassing – I can see why.

Second impressions are more positive; the many moving parts move smoothly and without measurable play, adjustments are easy and the various détente stops for commonly used angles are positive. A hold-down clamp is supplied – this isn't quite as firm in use as I would like – and a dust bag clips onto the extraction port. This works after a fashion, but obviously a vacuum extractor is the preferred option, especially in a client's kitchen.

Challenge

I thought that I'd give the saw a challenge for its first cut, so I dug out a well-seasoned piece of 75mm, 3in English oak, clamped it to the table, warily switched on and pulled the saw across. I needn't have worried. The 40-tooth TCT blade, fitted as standard, barely noticed that the oak was there and left the endgrain virtually polished. This experience was repeated with other hardwoods, softwoods and MDF cutting at all kinds of angles – clean, accurate and undramatic cutting.

So there you are; apart from the wobbly stand this tool will take some of the fear out of fitting. Lock it up though, on site the Sidekick attracted more admiring looks than I felt comfortable about, and it is very portable…

ABOVE: Dust bag works after a fashion... moving parts move smoothly

ABOVE LEFT: Escape from the workshop with a Sidekick

Delta 36-230 chopsaw

Colin Eden-Eadon tests Delta's 12in Sidekick compound mitre saw

BELOW: You can take it with you – Delta's 36-230

WHEN I OPENED the box and took out the instruction manual, much to my amazement it made sense and had clear photographs that were well labelled! Well done Delta – other manufacturers take note.

This saw, the bigger brother of the Delta Sidekick 36-250, reviewed on page 5, is designed for compound angle cutting of larger stock. Setting up is very easy: after clamping the machine to a bench, a lockpin releases the saw blade/ motor assembly ready for use. For longer term use the Delta could be permanently mounted.

The machine has a substantial feel to it, with a cast-aluminium base. It's heavy, and I'm not sure I'd want to lug it around too often unless I had a big job on. This weight does, however, provide stability in use and the machine's impressive versatility makes it worth carrying up a few sets of stairs.

Fully guarded

The saw's retractable guard will work only if a lever is depressed at the same time as the trigger switch is operated. This means that the saw is fully guarded even when not cutting – a sensible safety addition which isn't actually mentioned in this manual. The dustbag supplied is too small for lengthy use, but its port can be linked to a mobile extractor, handy when using the saw in a client's house.

The four-position cam lever clamp is a little tricky to operate at first, but firm enough with practice. Everything works smoothly, and the machine is easy to operate. Detente stops for 15°, 22.5°, 32.62° and 45° angles are provided and are very positive. The bevel lock handle is also substantial and positive.

FACTS AND FIGURES

Price	£472.28 including VAT – check with stockist for best price
Motor	1400W
Blade	304.8mm, 12in
Arbor	30mm
Speed	3500rpm
Crosscut capacity	203.2 x 63.5mm (8 x 2½in)
	177.8 x 88.9mm (7 x 3½in)
Mitre at 45° R&L	146.0 x 63.5mm (5¾ x 2½in)
Bevel at 45°L	165.1 x 63.5mm (6½ x 2½in)
	203.2 x 34.9mm (8 x 1⅜in)
Compound 45° x 45°	133.3 x 38.1mm (5¼ x 1½in)
	117.4 x .57.1mm (4⅝ x 2¼in)
Mitre indents	0°, 15°, 22.5°, 31.62°, 45° R&L
Bevel stops	0° and 45°

Availability: contact Delta UK, Westwings House, Station Road, Guiseley, W. Yorks LS20 8BX, tel 01943 873535, fax 01943 875959.

The 40-tooth TCT blade used on the test machine comes as standard and cuts superbly well, giving a clean finish to oak end-grain. I tried various compound angles in a variety of sizes and woods – all the timbers were cut very smoothly with no trouble.

The whole machine is very well put together and should prove a robust and accurate tool for a good many years. ■

![Delta advertisement showing a range of woodworking machines including bandsaws, sanders, scroll saws, mitre saws, grinders and drill presses, with the American flag and DELTA logo]

DECLARE YOUR INDEPENDENCE WITH DELTA

Biscuit assortment

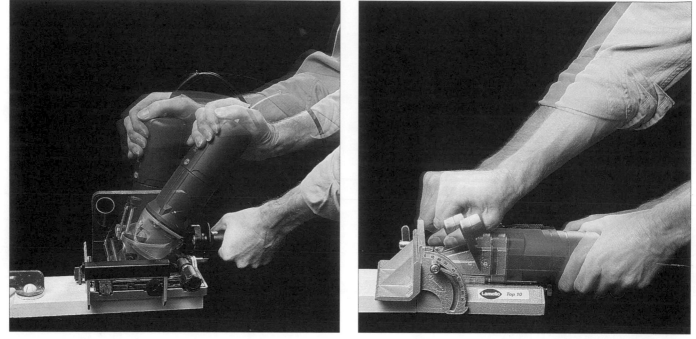

Editor **Paul Richardson** takes the plunge and puts 11 biscuit jointers to the test. Read how the cookies crumble...

PHOTOGRAPHY BY CHRIS SKARBON

THERE ARE just two basic types of biscuit jointer; the swing type, in which the motor is mounted on a pivot and the blade is swung into the work; and the plunge type in which the motor is mounted on a slide, the blade entering perpendicular to the work.

There's no question that the plunge approach has become the standard – only the Bosch and the DeWalt DW685K offer an alternative, and both are essentially very old models. Most people find that the direct action of plunging is more positive for general biscuiting, but for grooving, scribing and trimming the swing type has superior balance.

A four inch TCT blade has almost no run-out, so a swing jointer guided against a straight-edge leaves almost as good a finish when cutting sheet material as a panel saw. To exploit this Bosch offer a guide-rail for their GUF 422A, and DeWalt and others supply fine-finish blades for sawing.

Angle on fences

With the exception of the Skil, all the plunge jointers on test have fall-front fences which are adjustable from 0°, flush with the front plate, to 90°, parallel to the blade, allowing a wide range of mitred joints to be slotted from the inside of the mitre, *see photo*.

Most of these fall-fronts are of the Lamello type, having an additional right-angle fence which is adjustable for distance from the blade – to allow for various material thicknesses and non-flush joints. These are removable and reversible, having a 45° angle cast into their opposite faces.

This is used either to give more adjustment when indexing from the inside of the mitre, or in conjunction with the fall-front, to extend the range to 135° and beyond which allows indexing from the outside of a mitre.

A small 45° angle is also to be found at the inner corner of the right-angle

fence for quick mitre-jointing, *see photo*.

The Virutex and the DeWalt DW682K have a fall-front which is also adjustable for distance from the blade; no separate right-angle fence is needed, although without one maximum adjustment is 90°. DeWalt have, however, included the external mitre notch for 135°.

Ryobi's solution is a fall-front which is adjustable from 0° to 135° and for distance from the blade; the Skil has no fall-front, just a reversible 90°/45° fence.

The swing-type jointers have two very different fence arrangements. DeWalt fit a right-angle fence with simple distance-to-blade adjustment – good for grooving – and a 45° attachment for mitres.

Bosch have loaded their jointer with a variety of fence options, angles being accommodated by the baseplate pivoting in the same way as a fall-front. Swing jointers also have fine lateral adjustment of the blade within the body.

Lamello Top 10

Lamello started all this, and they still make the biscuit jointer to be seen with – instant workshop credibility comes with the green and red Top 10. Supplied in a – biscuit jointed – wooden case, the Top 10 has a fall front and right-angle fence giving it a full 180° of adjustment.

Oomph is supplied by a Metabo motor which is smooth and, at 750W, the most powerful on test; the six-tooth blade is Lamello's own and very nice too. The jointer has the advantage of a large range of accessories in the Lamello system. Engineering and finish are impeccable, but some users find the short body and heavy weight induce limp wrist syndrome. A real man's jointer.

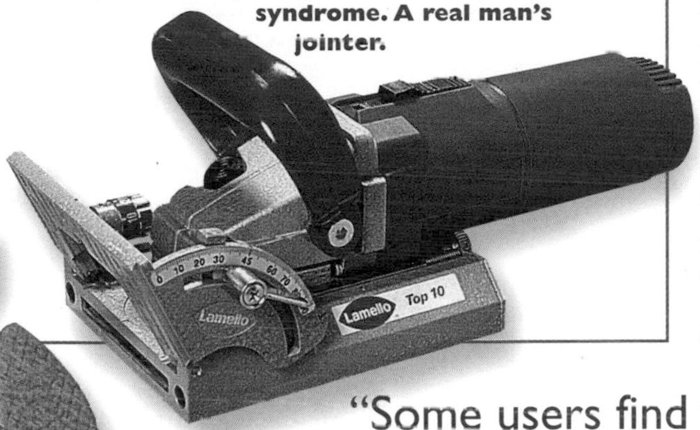

Lamello Classic

For the real man with the smaller wallet, Lamello offer this no frills version of the Top 10. Stripped of the green paint and some of the shiny bits, all of the other Top 10 features remain: excellent engineering quality, nice blade, Metabo motor – slightly less powerful at 705W – and versatile fence arrangement. It is supplied in a plastic case with a natty lift-out tray – much more useful than the Top 10's wooden box. It fits the extensive range of Lamello system accessories and costs £100 less than the Top 10 – that buys a lot of green Hammerite.

"Some users find the short body and heavy weight induce limp wrist syndrome"

Lamello Dynamic

The only cordless biscuit jointer available in the UK, this tool is also unique among those tested in having a direct drive for the blade. Right-angle drives are noisy, and this machine is a blessed relief after the clatter of the rest. The blade takes a short time to spin up to its operating speed, which at 24,000rpm is over twice as fast as the mains machines – this explains the two-tooth blade. Nicely balanced, free-cutting, Lamello's well-made fence is up front – a life-saver on site and the only jointer you can use with a hangover.

TOP LEFT: Mitre-jointing from the inside face using a fall fence

UPPER MIDDLE LEFT: Mitre-jointing from the outside face using notch on right-angle fence

LOWER MIDDLE LEFT: Typical fall- front with separate right-angle fence fitted – shown here reversed for mitre-jointing

BOTTOM LEFT: Plunge jointer with height-adjustable fall front

Makita 3901

With the exception of the swing-type machines, most biscuit jointers are either made by Lamello or look as if they were. The Makita , however, reveals evidence of thoughtful research and design which pays off in usability. Plunging occurs along two purposeful-looking steel rods, and the right-angle fence on the fall-front is adjusted by means of a knob-operated gear – nice. Best of all is a neat, hinged access plate for blade changing; it may not be needed very often, but shows that Makita care. Very usable, ergonomically sound and well-made, the one we'd most like to live with.

Skil 1810

There's no getting away from it, this jointer is predominantly constructed from plastic. This takes some getting used to, but there are benefits – chiefly low weight – and it ain't going to go rusty. With the baseplate flat on the work, the Skil's body sits high, which gives good clearance for knuckles but may contribute to the drive's high clatter factor. Fence is adjusted by Allen screws – a key for these is clipped into the rear of the baseplate – and offers 90° and 45°. Supplied in a vast plastic case with a nice glue bottle which has a biscuit slot-shaped nozzle.

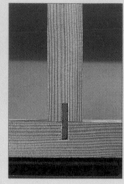

ABOUT BISCUITS

The principle of biscuiting is a simple one, with a clever twist. A saw blade is plunged into two edges to be jointed, leaving a shallow kerf in each part. Because the fence of a biscuit jointer indexes on the face of the work, these kerfs are exactly the same distance from their respective faces regardless of any difference in thickness – this makes the tool just as useful for corner joints, *see photos*, as for edge-to-edge work. Biscuits can also be set well away from an edge for 'T' joints, *see photo*, for divisions within carcasses and for shelves.

Having cut the slot, an oval biscuit of compressed beech is placed into the kerf with a small quantity of glue, the other kerf is glued and the two parts brought together... a perfectly flush joint results. Unlike a dowel, a biscuit will move slightly along its slot to allow for alignment, so around 6mm of tolerance is acceptable. This means that a pencil stroke across the offered-up joint is all that is needed for marking out, and the joint can be rubbed slightly to express surplus glue.

The twist is that the biscuits absorb the glue's moisture and swell, tightening the joint and reducing clamping time.

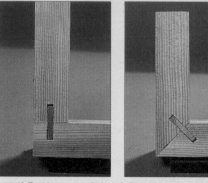

LEFT: Butt corner joint takes seconds with a biscuit or two
MIDDLE: Mitres don't take much longer
RIGHT: T joints good for carcass divisions and shelves

"When jointing it feels a bit like a saw, when sawing it feels a bit like a jointer"

Bosch GUF 422A

Is it a biscuit jointer or a saw? Both, of course. Quite bulky, the Bosch is light in weight which helps its handling. It will work with an optional guide rail for sawing; an eight-tooth blade is fitted for a clean finish. Build quality is good although there are quite a few plastic bits involved in the baseplate, which bristles with gadgets, fences and alternative mounting points for the handle. This machine will cut a sheet of MDF into components and then joint them together, so it isn't surprising that it suffers from a slight identity crisis – when jointing it feels a bit like a saw, when sawing it feels a bit like a jointer.

Ryobi JM100

When introduced, this jointer was the only alternative to the Lamello if you wanted a fall-front plunge jointer, and is still the only one to offer 135° adjustment without a second right-angle fence. Motor is quiet and powerful, but some find the small body awkward to hold. Only three depth settings are offered in a tool which demonstrates the usual good quality Ryobi manufacture - with the exception of the fence; this works adequately but is crude in comparison with the cast and machined aluminium examples on the other plunge jointers tested. A competent machine that would benefit from a redesign.

Virutex AB 11C

Looks more like a Lamello clone than it is - the fall-front is also adjustable for height, so no right-angle fence. The Virutex has a professional air to it; the components are well finished, the moving parts operate smoothly, a good six-tooth blade is fitted, altogether it feels as if it will last well. Balance is less than great, though; the motor casing is long *and* wide - and at 3.2kg, it wins the heaviest machine on test award. One major snag: the dust extraction port is narrow and ill-placed - MDF dust goes through it, but solid wood waste doesn't.

DeWalt DW685K

The oldest swing jointer design on the market, a simple machine with a proven motor pivoting in a well-cast and machined chassis, both faces of which are trued for use as register surfaces. Additional fence consists of two rods and a flat bar; awkward to adjust but solid when locked and ideal for grooving. Fine adjustment facility positions the blade laterally in the chassis. For mitred joints a 45° fence is supplied which allows the whole jointer to be tilted. Not much to it, but it does what it does faultlessly and a lot of people won't use anything else.

> "Extraction connector occasionally falls off to send a shower of dust up the operator's sleeve"

Freud JS102

It's hard not to admire the Freud biscuit jointer if only for its audacity. Their first model, the JS100, had a fixed front with a 90°/45° fence; it was a little rough round the edges but performed well and undercut the competition by a mile, bringing biscuit jointing within the reach of everyone. Now they have a fall-front model with all the bells and whistles. Blade quality benefits from Freud's core business – making tooling – the motor is a little noisy but has adequate power, all the moving parts move as they should. Motor casing is bulky but weight is low at 2.8kg – and who cares at this price.

DeWalt DW682K

This is a plunge machine from the only manufacturer apart from Lamello to market more than one jointer. The fall-front is adjustable for height by a snazzy rack and pinion and includes a notch for external mitres – the hole in the fence is too big for small work, though, and requires a sub-fence to be made. Plunge action and depth adjustment are smooth, the 600W motor feels powerful and is operated by a trigger switch under the casing – be careful when you pick it up. Handling and balance very good indeed, the only real drawback is an extraction connector which occasionally falls off to send a shower of dust up the operator's sleeve.

SOUTHPAWS, HEAVYWEIGHTS AND KNUCKLE-BRUISERS

The mains-powered Lamellos, DeWalt's DW685K, the Bosch and the Virutex have centrally-mounted slide switches suitable for left- and right-handed use; the cordless Lamello and DeWalt's DW682K have equally ambidextrous triggers. All other machines on test have left-mounted slide switches – perfect for right-hand thumb operation but awkward for left-handers.

Weight and comfort of handling are important factors as extended use of biscuit jointers, especially plunge-type machines, can impose a strain on the user – swing jointers tend to be rested on the work while plunge types overhang it; the lever action of swinging is also easier than a direct push.

Most users ignore the handles fitted to plunge jointers, instead gripping the motor body with one hand and the fence with the other, so a long motor body is more comfortable. Lamello's Top 10 and Classic have short bodies and are among the heaviest machines on test – their long blade housing also shortens the effective hand room and can be hard on the knuckles. The Virutex's long body doesn't make up for its bulk and weight, though.

DeWalt's DW682K has a slim handle profile to the rear of its motor casing and above its trigger switch – only this machine and Lamello's Dynamic make any real provision for use by humans. The lightest plunge jointer on test is the Skil, with a long, narrow motor body and good clearance which make it the most comfortable to use for long periods.

ABOVE: If there's an overall best on test, this is it

Conclusion:

Biscuit joints have been around for over 40 years but most power tool manufacturers ignored the fact for the first 30 – then they realised it was a good way of shifting motors and right-angle drives developed for angle-grinders and sanders.

We've tried almost all of the machines available in the UK –

Lamello make several others and Atlas Copco have recently introduced a fall-front plunge model – and some of them feel like… angle-grinders. This still leaves a good choice for all levels of user, though, and the price range is wider than it used to be.

For dual-purpose use the **Bosch GUF 422A** offers

versatility, but don't ignore the **DW685K**. This has limited facilities but is fiendishly accurate and will take years of hard use without complaint.

Beginners and the budget-conscious can do a lot worse than the bargain-priced **Freud JS102**. It has all the features of the more expensive machines and makes a good spare jointer in the pro workshop.

In the mid-range it's a fight between the **Makita 3901** and **DeWalt's DW682K**. Both are high performers; the DeWalt is more comfortable, the Makita more sophisticated.

Up at the top? £100 seems a lot to pay for some green paint so we'd go for the **Classic** – and if you need a cordless there's no choice at all, just the **Dynamic**; luckily this is no hardship.

Overall favourite depends on whether anyone's looking – if they are then the **Top 10** is the Haute Couture of jointers, but alone in the workshop I'd rather use the **Makita 3901**. ∎

FACTS AND FIGURES

BRAND	MODEL	WATTAGE	WEIGHT	TEETH	PRICE*	DISTRIBUTION
Lamello	Top 10	750W	3.1kg	6	£469	JKO Ltd tel 01494 521051, fax 01494 461176
Lamello	Classic	705W	3.1kg	6	£368	JKO Ltd tel 01494 521051, fax 01494 461176
Lamello	Dynamic	N/A 12V	2.5kg	2	£455	JKO Ltd tel 01494 521051, fax 01494 461176
Makita	3901	590W	2.8kg	6	£298	Makita UK Ltd tel 01908 211678, fax 01908 211400
Skil	1810	550W	2.5kg	4	£222	Skil Power Tools tel 01895 838743, fax 01895 838802
Ryobi	JM100	600W	3.0kg	6	£351	Ryobi Power Equipment (UK) Ltd tel 01452 724777, fax 01452 727400
Bosch	GUF 422A	620W	2.4kg	8	£328	Robert Bosch Ltd tel 01895 838412, fax 01895 838418
Virutex	AB 11C	650W	3.2kg	6	£264	Ney Ltd tel 01203 694794, fax 01203 695005
DeWalt	DW682K (plunge)	600W	3.0kg	6	£337	Black & Decker UK Ltd tel 01753 567055, fax 01753 572112
DeWalt	DW685K (swing)	600W	2.8kg	6	£442	Black & Decker UK Ltd tel 01753 567055, fax 01753 572112
Freud	JS102	710W	2.8kg	6	£257	Freud Tooling UK Ltd tel 0113 245 3737, fax 0113 243 8883

* List price including VAT. Not very meaningful these days, shop around for best deal

NOTHING CUTS QUICKER, SMOOTHER, FINER, BETTER!

The RE-601 router is Ryobi's latest addition to a comprehensive range of woodworking equipment. With its powerful 2,050 Watt motor, variable speed and soft start it can cope with even the largest cutters.

Ryobi's long tradition of innovation in woodworking means there's sure to be a Ryobi product that's just right for you.

Rugged, reliable Ryobi. Quality that means you do a good job - better.

| CM-31 CHAIN MORTISER | AP-10N THICKNESSER | BT-3000 TABLE SAW | OSS-450 OSCILLATING SPINDLE SANDER | L-282 PLANER | W-6610 CIRCULAR SAW | BE-424 BELT SANDER | BDM-1200 'TORQUEFORCE' 12 V CORDLESS DRILL/DRIVER | TS-221 MITRE SAW |

RYOBI

Portable power

Can cordless drills be too powerful?
Technical Editor **Alan Goodsell** puts
three super-charged newcomers to the test

CORDLESS DRILLS have come a long way in recent years.

Battery and DC motor technology has taken a great leap from the lowly 7.2V models to the extremely powerful 12 to 18.5V drills now on offer, but I feel that this new breed of drills is nearing the limit at which the current design can be safely used.

Their ergonomics, and habits of use, are based on the original low-powered drills; these didn't have the huge amount of torque which these newer tools possess. The fact is that cordless drills are no longer merely low-powered versions of their corded cousins; but these new, powerful models are still used with the same care-free attitude.

We instinctively respect a tool that has to be plugged in to the mains supply before use; the act of doing this acts as a reminder and concentrates the mind.

We carry these newer cordless drills round like a hand tool; the pressure of finger on trigger is all it takes to release considerable power. A large diameter wood bit can be planted into a piece of wood without a thought being given to the effect of immense torque or how to combat it.

The operator may suddenly find a heavy battery swinging around to make damaging contact with fragile human body parts. These tools should really have cross-han-

dles like those on corded drills, so that the user has something to hang on to when bracing against torque. Some kind of 'pre-flight' check, like the thumb button on a Skilsaw, would help to alert the user that something potentially dangerous was about to happen.

MAKITA 631DWAE 12V

The Makita 12V model is claimed to have five times the life of other cordless drills, but the only apparent evidence of this is seen in the externally replaceable brushes. The brushes are normally the first parts to wear out, effectively ending the life of the drill.

Although not of the highest voltage, this drill has bags of power in both of its speed ranges. Long trigger travel provides good control of the variable speed; when released quickly the brake bites fast.

For a cordless, the motor is quite noisy at lower speeds, but quietens as speed increases.

It has the lightest torque release I've seen on a cordless drill/driver, and on the lowest setting is ideal for placing the tiny screws required for hinges.

This lightness of touch follows through in the 18-position torque range, but the highest setting is perhaps too light for larger screws, leaving their heads proud; if set on the fixed setting for drilling, though, it will pull in almost any size screw.

Well balanced

The drill is well balanced and comfortable, the forward and reverse push-pull switch being perfectly placed for my thumb and index finger.

The keyless 13mm, $^{1}/_{2}$in chuck is mostly plastic and so feels a bit tacky.

Bright red batteries are easy to find among piles of sawdust, and they charge within an hour in a charger that has more status monitor lights than the Starship Enterprise's dashboard.

Makita claims this excellent, well-balanced and powerful drill will long outlive the competition. Time will tell.
- **Price:** £350 including VAT.
- **Availability:** For your nearest supplier contact Makita (UK) Ltd. Michigan Drive, Tongwell, Milton Keynes, Bucks MK15 8JD, tel 01908 211678, fax 01908 211400.

RYOBI T144-2 14.4V

The new Ryobi cordless drill/driver may have climbed the next rung of the voltage ladder to 14.4V but its usable power

ABOVE: The Ryobi T144-2 – 24 torque settings if you need them

LEFT: The Makita 6313DWAE – five times the life?

"Prolonged use of this drill will develop muscles like Popeye's – without the ➤ spinach"

FACTS AND FIGURES

	Makita 6313DWAE	Ryobi T144-2	Elu BSA82KA
Price inc. VAT	£350	£327	£434
Chuck capacity	13mm, $^1/_2$in	10mm, $^3/_8$	13mm, $^1/_2$in
Drilling capacity:			
Wood	25mm, 1in	19mm, $^3/_4$in	38mm, 1$^1/_2$in
Steel	13mm, $^1/_2$in	10mm, $^3/_8$in	16mm, $^5/_8$in
Motor voltage	12V DC	14.4V DC	18V DC
No load speed			
Lo	0 – 450rpm	0 – 350rpm	0 – 400rpm
Hi	0 – 1,400rpm	0 – 1,200rpm	0 – 1.200rpm
Clutch	18 position	24 position	14 position
Net weight	2.0kg inc. battery	2.0kg inc. battery	2.6kg inc. battery

doesn't seem to have increased much, the drill running out of steam before the heaviest torque setting released while winding in 85mm, 3$^1/_2$in No. 8 screws.

Of the incredible 23 torque settings, the lowest and highest are about right, but the huge range in between is a bit excessive.

Just behind the Hi/Lo speed switch is a spirit level which is handy for drilling as it works with the drill vertical or horizontal.

The Ryobi is a little nose heavy, and I found the handle slightly too fat and squarish for comfort. Changing from forward to reverse is easy, though, with a convenient through-the-body push-pull switch.

Quiet and smooth

A long trigger gives good control of the variable speeds, and the brake stops the drill almost instantly.

The motor is quiet and smooth, but the plastic 10mm, $^3/_8$in keyless chuck is small for a drill of this voltage. Might this be because a 13mm, $^1/_2$in chuck

would only highlight the slight lack of power?

The high performance batteries can be recharged in under an hour, and a lanyard clipped to the handle proves useful when two hands are needed to hold a job while the drill is close to hand.
- **Price:** £327 including VAT.
- **Availability:** For your nearest supplier contact Ryobi Power Equipment (UK) Ltd, Pavilion 1, Olympus Park Business Centre, Quedgeley, Gloucs GL2 6NF, tel 01452 724777, fax 01452 727400.

ELU BSA82KA 18V

The Elu is the biggest and baddest of the cordless drill/driver world, excluding the specialist 24V units which are quite different in appearance and use. Incorrect use of its immense power could well twist a shoulder out of its socket.

With its large battery the drill is understandably heavy; although it is well balanced, prolonged use soon provokes a throbbing arm ache. The drill can, however, be stood on the battery, making the tool easy to pick up and keeping the air vents out of the dust.

Surprisingly for a drill of this size and power, the torque setting at the low end is almost perfect; but on the fifth setting a large screw can be wound right through a piece of softwood before releasing.

The familiar, through-the-body forward and reverse switch is well placed but a bit stiff, the trigger giving good proportional control of the speed.

Only one hand is needed to operate the 13mm, 1/2in chuck

because it has only one moving part to turn, unlike others that need a two-handed Chinese-burn type action to operate.

A free-spinning nose on the chuck protects the work if it is accidentally touched while running.

The motor is quiet, and the variable speed is smooth through its range in both forward and reverse.

This drill offers an impressive amount of power and huge torque while retaining the ability for fine work, but prolonged use will develop muscles like Popeye's – without the spinach.
- **Price:** £434 including VAT.
- **Availability:** For your nearest supplier contact Elu Power Tools Ltd, 210 Bath Road, Slough, Berks SL1 1YD, tel 01753 576717, fax 01753 521312.

Conclusion

As expected, these drills have many features in common: keyless chucks, variable speed, forward and reverse, screwdriver bits, torque action and carrying cases.

All come well equipped with two batteries and a fast charger to allow continuous use.

They are all good tools, each boasting something to set it apart from the others, and I found them all to have plenty of power for the type of work I do.

But the time cannot be far off when the awesome power of 18V will become the industry standard, leaving manufacturers to look at the next step up. I hope they will start to include some safety measures to combat the hefty torque that these machines will possess.

BELOW: The Elu BSA82KA - 38mm, 1 1/2in capacity in wood from a cordless tool

LEFT: These powerful nail guns are best used two-handed to avoid recoil

RIGHT: Dent-free pinning of mouldings in the workshop or on-site

Projects Editor **Colin Eden-Eadon** looks at a new range of nail guns from Maestri

Quick on the drawer

ONE TIME a sales representative came to the Barnsley workshops and suggested that we might like a nail gun. "What for?" he was asked, "You could staple the backs into the furniture," he replied; he was lucky he didn't retreat to the thud of chisels being buried into the door behind him!

With the advance of technology and increased precision, however, nail guns are no longer the preserve of roofers and builders, but have become accepted in the cabinet shop.

Now Maestri of Italy's portable answers to the problems created by air tools are available in the UK. The range includes several guns which work directly off a 240V mains supply as well as 110V for site use.

I tested staple/brad combination, and panel-pinner models.

ME 404/6

This combination version incorporates heavier gauge staples and brads in one machine, and is intended for general use such as floor-laying, building, carpentry and upholstery.

Solidly built, this tool has a quality feel. Rubber feet protect the finish of the job surface being worked on, and it comes with a plastic carrying case.

The blunt-ended brads reduce the risk of splitting the material; their small heads mean there is little making good to be done. Such is the power of delivery, the brads punch in by 2mm ($^5/_{64}$in).

It worked well in softwoods,

birch ply and hardwoods, but I experienced some kickback when the machine was used single-handed on harder materials.

A natty front piece extracts misfired brads and staples – but turn off at the mains first!

The large, full-hand trigger is equipped with a safety lock mechanism to prevent accidental firing.

For planting on mouldings this is an invaluable tool – and it would also be useful when jig-making

ME30/8

This panel-pinner is designed with fitters, installers and cabinetmakers in mind, and delivers a range of different sized panel pins.

This latest version features a specially angled nylon nose to protect glass when installing glazing bars. The accuracy and positive action of the delivery means that extremely fine work can be pinned safely – much less risk than when using a pin-hammer.

Conclusion

The model numbers in the range are somewhat confusing – the 404/6 tested also going under the number 606 – but it includes a more conventional stapler designed for upholsterers. All extremely well built, these tools should prove to be a boon in most workshops, and can be taken on site as easily as a power drill – a must when fitting furniture. ■

> "Nail guns are no longer the preserve of roofers and builders"

FACTS & FIGURES

ME404/6 combination
Price	£170.37 including VAT
Magazine capacity	130mm
Maximum theoretical speed	2 shots/second
Maximum average output	20 shots/minute
Weight	1.6 kg
Staples (6mm width)	12, 18, 22, 26mm
Brads (18 gauge)	15, 19, 25mm

ME30/8 mini pinner
Price	£246.75 including VAT
Magazine capacity	130mm
Maximum theoretical speed	3 shots/second
Maximum average output	30 shots/minute
Weight	1.4 kg
Pins (21/08 gauge)	15, 20, 25, 30mm

Available from: Maestri-Kear (UK) Ltd, Little Mannings, Winterpit Lane, Mannnings Heath, Horsham, West Sussex, RH13 6LZ, tel 01403 275575, fax 01403 271270.

"Never has handrail jointing been so easy or reliable!"

Dovetails from Hoffmann

Anthony Bailey is impressed with this dovetail jointing machine

SOME YEARS AGO a dovetail jointing system called the Titman 'Wedgelock' appeared on the market, sporting a German-built Kress motor. The basis of the system was a neat double-dovetail 'key'.

This must have been a German Shepherd in British Bulldog's clothing, for here we have the Hoffmann MU 2 dovetail jointing machine, a high precision, well built and engineered product.

The idea behind it is simple enough; the machine cuts dovetail slots into components, which are then joined together by the insertion of wood or plastic double-dovetail keys.

This principle lends itself to production work with stacks of identical components, but for this it has to offer good and repeatable accuracy.

Operation

The machine has a well finished aluminium cast base with a nicely milled top that gives a perfect working surface onto which are fitted the various operating components. A cast arm fitted to a pull-down stroke lever works by applying a crank action to the moveable parts.

Pulling on the lever first pushes and secures an ingenious hold-down onto the workpiece; further effort switches on and raises a router motor mounted at the rear, pulling up a dovetail cutter into the workpiece to make a dovetail slot.

Virtually in an instant one half of the joint is cut, the other half being produced in the same way.

A depth stop, using a metric scale, allows a large degree of adjustment in slot length.

For mitred joints Hoffmann supply a black-finished piece of alloy machined at 45° to serve as a guide, together with a number of other guides to cope with various jointing angles.

These fit into a centre slot on the table and are adjusted with a sprung lift-and-turn lever.

With this in place, and given properly cut mitres or butt joints, accurate alignment of components is guaranteed.

External guides enable same-size pieces to be fed between ➤

ABOVE AND RIGHT: Simple but effective jointing with dovetail keys

guides for reliable results, and for repeat cuts at specific lengths swing-down stops can be attached to add-on extension rails.

Stick-on scales can be fitted into a groove for lining up long workpieces if the machine is permanently installed on a made-up bed.

'Keys' range

So, with an extensive range of plastic and wood dovetail 'keys', different size cutters and various guides including a mullion jig, it is possible to make incredibly strong and accurate joints for a wide variety of work.

The MU 2 seems a natural for mitred work, but it will tackle items such as jointing handrailing, including turns and handrail-to-newel posts.

For this simply raise the router and adjust the depth stop to lock the motor at the correct height above the work surface. Guides removed, 'drop' the work sideways onto the cutter, sliding it along the fence until the appropriate slot length has been formed, then ditto on the other piece. Never has handrail jointing been so easy or reliable!

In use

The machine comes with a standard cutter factory-set for depth, so starting work is easy.

In-service adjustment is made by unclamping and fractionally moving the actual motor body. Guide setting and work holding via the pull-down operating lever is a cinch, while cutting the dovetail is almost a non event, the cutter zipping through the wood; however, a second pass is necessary to clear the chipping created by the first.

Having cut the joint the 'keys' are easily fitted with the application of a spot of glue and a tap with a rubber-faced hammer.

Noise compares with that from any small router, and extraction isn't an issue either because the minimal waste stays at the rear of the workpiece.

The rear cast-on tray with its ribbed rubber base is handy for stowing spare cutters, dovetail keys and anti-spelch inserts.

Conclusion

There aren't many end-to-end or framing jobs that the Hoffmann can't handle. Most mitre or butt joints are up for grabs, and it can cope with such awkward items as picture frames and cornices at a speed which makes other 'quick' methods look leisurely.

This machine should find a home in any workshop where quick and repetitious joint work is required.

The MU2 is not cheap, with a starting price of £1,398 including VAT, plus the inevitable extras, but its capacity to take on precision repetition work makes it a very attractive proposition.

BELOW: Wide range of guides and accessories

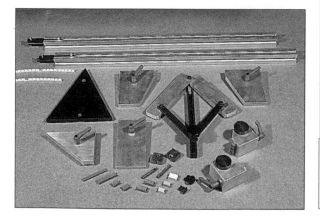

FACTS AND FIGURES

Max. cutting height	80mm, $3^{1}/_{8}$in
Overall dimensions	580 x 420 x 670mm, 23 x $16^{1}/_{2}$ x $26^{1}/_{2}$in
Weight	32kg, 70lb
Collet speed	6mm or $^{1}/_{4}$in
Speed	27,000rpm
List Price	MU 2 Manual £1,398 inc. VAT
	MU 2P Pneumatic £2,009 inc. VAT
Cutters	
example	6mm TCT, £24 inc. VAT
Dovetail keys	
example	W-2 14mm plastic without end cap: £49 per 1000 inc. VAT
	W-3 80mm plastic without end cap: £95 per 1000 inc. VAT
Contact:	Hoffmann Machine Co. Ltd, Lane Head, Mewith High Bentham, Nr Lancaster LA2 7DL Tel: 01524 262500 Fax: 01524 262220

Editor **Paul Richardson** makes up for lost time testing a vacuum veneering system

It's in the bag

REGULAR READERS of F&C will know that I'm an exponent of hammer veneering and have Scotch glue running through my veins. For many years this traditional method has been my mainstay; with it I have laid thousands of square feet of assorted veneer onto hundreds of pieces of furniture.

Of course, while hand-veneering is eminently suitable for the tricky stuff where a lot of matching and crossbanding is called for, there is no great joy in hand-applying large quantities of simple edge-matched veneer to big square bits of MDF. So when a lot of carcass sides and the like are called for, they are taken to a local firm's eight-by-four hot press.

It had occurred to me that there should be a reliable method of veneering that falls between these two extremes, but while I was aware of vacuum systems I confess that I had never tried one. Prompted by Andrew Skelton's fondness for the plastic bag as a veneering device, I thought that it was about time I did.

Affordable

The Air Press Company produce a small range of self-contained, affordable vacuum systems that have found favour with many F&C contributors and readers. Smallest is the Standard, featuring a 1200 by 1200mm (4 by 4ft) bag and a neat little pump; next is the Professiona l, supplied with one 2400 by 1200mm (8 by 4ft) bag – although it can run three of these simultaneously – and a meaty 6 cu.m. per hour maintenance-free pump.

We tested the top of the range Autopro, essentially a Professional with the addition of a pressure-sensitive switch which turns the pump on and off as required to maintain the vacuum.

This keeps the noise down, but interestingly all pumps supplied by Air Press are capable of running against a total vacuum almost indefinitely, and require no maintenance.

All the bits and pieces required – hose, connectors and so on – are supplied with the package and are of good quality. I won't ramble on about putting the thing together, but special mention should be made of the through-the-bag connector – a purpose-made aluminium component – and the plastic closure strip, both of which are well thought out and effective.

And how's this for comprehensive supply? Also included is a heavy-duty metal punch for making the hole in the bag.

Additional bags are available in standard sizes up to 3600 by 1200mm (12 by 4ft) and in larger sizes to order

Compact

I hadn't realised just how compact the system was until it arrived; everything except the 1350mm closure strips could be stored quite easily under the ➤

ABOVE: This compact unit can cope with three 2400mm by 1200mm vacuum bags (one supplied as standard)

BELOW: Neat through-the-bag connector – note the substantial punch for cutting the hole

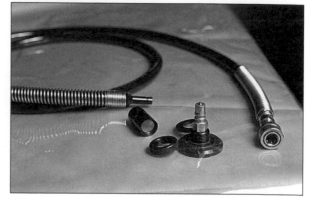

average kitchen sink – more than can be said for a hot press. Initial assembly takes less than five minutes.

Slipping a board of sheet material – MDF is best if heavy – into the bag provides a base on which work and formers can be placed, see 'Pressing Issues', *F&C* No 9.

A large former such as the one seen in the photographs will act as its own baseboard, though, especially if someone has just cut the intended board in half.

In the absence of a baseboard a path for the vacuum to act along is provided by a strip of breather fabric, also available from Air Press.

The former shown is the male half of a two-part example made for conventional use with clamps; the comparative ease with which it can be used in the vacuum bag is an eye opener – people with vacuum presses probably undertake a lot more curved work than the rest of us, just because they can. I found

myself considering things that could be made easily using this method, that I would be reluctant to undertake otherwise.

Flat veneering is even more straightforward. This does require a baseboard, the ground-work and veneer being placed face down on this, or another board being put on top as a caul.

It is a good idea to put the work into a plastic bag before it goes into the press, as it can be tedious clearing out the surplus glue from the vacuum bag.

I found a slight tendency for the bag to move the veneer as it pulls down unless a caul is used – Air Press recommend offcuts of vinyl flooring for this, these also being suitable for curved work.

It's a winner

The Air Press doesn't make my hammer and glue pot redundant, as I prefer to build up complex panels in 'real time', cutting through to make each join while the Scotch glue is still wet. Some

of my veneering is carried out when the piece of furniture is partially assembled, and again this rules out everything but Scotch.

For relatively straightforward lay-ups, though, the vacuum press wins hands down over a drive to the hot press. Curved laminating and the subsequent veneering of curved panels is easier using the bag than by any other method, and this opens up some interesting possibilities.

In fact having had the Air Press around for a short while, I can't understand why I didn't buy one years ago. Even the deluxe Autopro is affordable for a small cabinet workshop, and with another couple of bags pressing could be undertaken for other makers.

Personally I fancy having a go at a macassar ebony Ruhlmann table with a serpentine base, on display at Brighton Art Gallery and Museum, just the job for the vacuum press…

FACTS AND FIGURES

Model	Standard	Professional	Autopro
Bag size	1200 by 1200mm	2400 by 1200mm	2400 by 1200mm
Price inc VAT	£399.50	£585.15	£763.75

● **Contact: The Air Press Company, 148 Coombe Road, Salisbury, Wiltshire, SP2 8BL, tel/fax 01722 330224**

Centauro SP400

Anthony Bailey visits a UK supplier to test an Italian-made bandsaw

● Following an early career as a professional photographer, ANTHONY BAILEY established a furniture restoration business in Tunbridge Wells, later turning to cabinetmaking. He now combines this with consultancy work and writing on the subject of furniture making, joinery and equipment.

THE SP400 IS the smallest of the Centauro range, but built to the standard of its big-brother bandsaws. With some extra cash added to its £999 price tag to pay for necessary extras this would be a truly class machine, and it is easy to see why Scott & Sergeant, *see panel*, think it worth re-introducing.

The case work is of heavy gauge pressed steel; the back of the machine forms a box column for complete rigidity. This attention to stiffness is repeated with the welded criss-cross spines which are situated inside the case behind the wheels.

The finish is in two-tone hammered green enamel. Very few parts are made of plastic, the exceptions being the lock knobs, switch casing and dust outlet.

Three door sections, each with a knob, are employed to open the case. The upper and lower ones have a simple latch with no means of preventing the device from turning 360° and unlatching.

The narrow centre door covers the blade path; a screw thread holds the other two doors closed; a micro switch disables the electrics.

Saw table

The saw table is a reassuring piece of ground cast iron with a non-dovetailed slideway for the mitre fence; dust drops through holes in a round wooden blade insert.

The table is bolted down firmly onto the case below, with no provision for bevel cutting. A tilting table block is available for this function, but in practice bevel cutting would not be needed for most production purposes.

Bandwheels

The bandwheels are of cast steel; on the test machine a balance weight was added to the upper wheel. Steel driving bands are

fitted to the wheels with the customary camber on the running surface.

On top of the case is a large blade tension knob which sets against a metric scale. The blade tilt knob is in the usual place on the back of the upper case; a rather sharp plastic lock lever is at its base.

The machine can be easily freewheeled by hand to get the tracking right. Curiously, a strange squealing is evident when doing this. The offender is a beech block located in a pressed steel socket; this rubs against the blade, acting apparently as some

sort of cut-price blade brake. The absence of a proper electric brake is regrettable.

The lower blade and wheel have a brush to keep the dust from sticking.

Bearing guides

Coming to the table again, the blade above it is covered by an all-encompassing and very effective pressed steel telescopic guard.

The geared rise and fall for the bearing guides is linked to the guard, one large bearing behind and two bevelled steel wheels either side providing guidance

ABOVE RIGHT:
A workmanlike bandsaw.

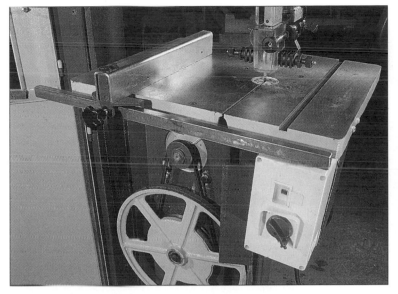

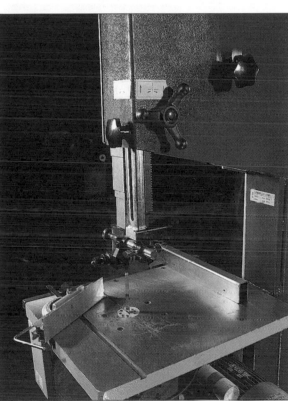

ABOVE: Very effective steel blade guard.

LEFT: Guard and guides operated by large tristar wheel – encourages safe use.

"The offender is a beech block located in a pressed steel socket; this rubs against the blade, acting apparently as some sort of cut-price blade brake"

with full adjustment and locking.

The mountings and adjustments are of a very tough grade of plastic, so probably more reliable than alloy castings.

Actual rise and fall for the guard and guides is provided by a large easy to turn tristar wheel, encouraging safe use of the bandsaw.

Fences

The table fence is very tough 'U' section pressed steel with no adjustment for true. Sideways adjustment is rather simple, and provides for no scale or fine setting; realistically, however, ➤

FACTS AND FIGURES

Manufacturer	Centauro, Limidi, Italy
Model	SP400
Motor power	1.1kW as fitted, variants available
Wheels	400mm x 2
Cutting height (under guides)	250mm, 10in
Cut width	385mm, 15$\frac{1}{4}$in
Speed	980rpm
Table size	500 x 400mm, 20 x 16in
Table/machine tilt	Fixed
Accessories supplied	Tool set, mitre gauge, fence
Accessories available	Tilting table block, single or three phase motors, precision bottom guide
Price	£999 excluding VAT
Information	Scott & Sergeant 01403 273000

IN ORDER TO test the Centauro I visited the suppliers, Scott & Sergeant of Horsham, West Sussex. For anyone not familiar with S & S, it is worth a brief description of who they are and what they do.

Scott & Sergeant are world-wide dealers and retailers in woodworking machinery. Rows and rows of new and second-hand gigantic machinery stand amid the dark, cavernous gloom of their industrial unit, ready to be inspected by prospective customers, thence to be plucked skyward by one of two enormous bright yellow gantry cranes to the accompaniment of exhortations to "mind your heads!"

Finally, the chosen article is transferred to the loading doors ready for shipment by lorry.

I was struck by the condition of some of the newly arrived equipment. Ancient, rusting Gorgons of old saws, planers, moulders, etc. take on a new lease of life when dealt with by the skilled hands of S & S engineers.

By the time they leave again, these machines are transmogrified into streamlined Sirens, shiny and finished in that universal, slightly pastel shade of engineering green.

One of the engineers told me that most reconditioned machines now go to the Third World, where the reliability, availability and low cost of spares is valued; in Europe we have to cope with complex CNC units and associated repair costs; worst of all, the increasingly tortuous nature of EC safety regulations means many of the older machines cannot be adapted. Rather naively I suggested that working on this scale, S & S weren't really interested in selling smaller equipment.

Wrong! S & S say large machines are difficult to shift and that they will gladly sell anything from a chop saw to a palm sander.

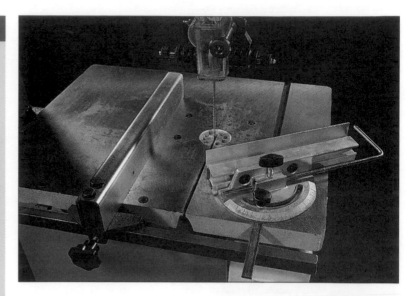

ABOVE: Little support to outboard of mitre slide.

RIGHT: Behind the lower door – good cast wheels driven by single speed pulley.

"I would certainly put this machine on my shortlist as it behaves well and is designed for a long working life"

this is adequate as few would trust a scale on a bandsaw fence.

The mitre fence works well, although the slot is not going to hold it down as a dovetailed slideway would, nor is there much support when cutting mitres as most of the table area is to the inside of the blade. Lastly, the extrusion mounted on the mitre slide is not true and doesn't sit flat on the table; this would be better replaced by a wood facing.

Blade removal can be effected with the fence guide in place, though as space to get the blade past the switch is limited, unbolting the guide may be easier.

Guides

The motor pulley allows just one speed with a fairly light section 'V' belt to transmit power from the meaty 1.1kW motor.

With the blade adjusted for proper running, and the teeth hanging off the edge of the wheels, the lower guide set does not come quite far enough forward.

In fact the lower bearing and its guide blocks are not nearly as good as the upper ones. Much more satisfactory would be the precision set – available as an extra.

A steel swing-out cover protects the blade in this area. The dial-type on-off switch is located under the table to the right.

A sprung push-in nib at the end reveals a slot to take a padlock, and a rubber-booted overload button.

On test

Apart from the needless and slightly distressing squeal from

the beech rubbing block, the Centauro has an acceptable sound level. When shown a large section of hardwood, it copes effortlessly with deep cutting.

The SP400's fence works well too; with no 'lead' on the blade, it cuts straight and true. The case fills with dust very quickly, though, so extraction would be a must for constant working.

Conclusion

I would certainly put this machine on my shortlist as it behaves well and is designed for a long working life. The only slight flies in the ointment are the lack of a proper electric brake, the poor lower guides and an add-on, rather than built-in tilt facility. These omissions can be rectified – at a price. ▪

Emco Cäsar 1 D450 bandsaw

Technical Editor **Alan Goodsell** sees red, but he gives this machine the green light

BELOW: The new Cäsar 1 bandsaw

RIGHT: A large cast-iron bed has geared tilt setting

BELOW RIGHT: Sturdy parallel fence is swung around to facilitate blade changing

AFTER A PERIOD spent concentrating on metalworking machines, Emco are re-establishing themselves in the UK woodworking market.

The striking red livery of the Austrian company's new range presents a radical departure from the familiar green of most woodworking machines – but at least they won't be walked into by mistake!

Construction

The big and sturdy Cäsar 1 bandsaw combines the features of two Scheppach models. It is based on their 2-speed version, but is fitted with a cast-iron bed taken from their 4-speed model.

This solidly built and smooth tilting cast-iron bed is well supported on an angular, heavy gauge steel chassis.

The large, spoked bandsaw wheels are coated with a substantial rubber tyre.

Bed

The big cast-iron bed has a plastic insert plate, and can be tilted 47° outboard and, unusually and usefully, 20° inboard. The geared tilt mechanism fitted is a delight, even though a trip to the rear of the machine is required.

To operate the tilt, two ratchet levers are released and a large plastic knob is turned, engaging a cog on the curved rack attached to the bed. This enables precise adjustments to be made when setting to the required angle.

It moves unimpeded when tipped away to 47°, but to tilt it to the 20° inward setting a small stop has to be flipped out of the way – a small price to pay for these advanced tilting capabilities. The stop can be adjusted to fine tune the 0° bed angle – a nice touch.

The large calibration scale proved to be an accurate guide for setting the bed angle; tightening the ratchet levers fixes the bed firmly in position.

Fences

A well-made, all-aluminium parallel fence runs smoothly on a tubular guide rail, and flipping down an easy to reach lever locks the fence firmly in place.

A magnifying lens set into the fence slide makes a calibration recessed into the guide rail easy to see.

Although an accessory is available, controlled fine adjusting of the fence is not provided as standard – but freehand alterations can easily be made.

The fence is faced with an L-shaped extrusion, with a thick and

"Undo a pair of clasp catches and the large door swings open, aided by a gas ram which operates like a CD ejecting from a stereo"

thin leg which can be attached in either of two positions, depending on stock thickness. It can also be slid back and fore to facilitate all types of sawing, including ripping. ➤

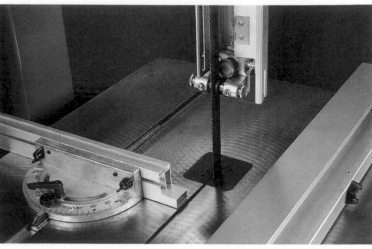

ABOVE: Blade
tensioning is made
easy with a tension
indicator

ABOVE RIGHT:
Good to see proper
blade guides

BELOW: Two speeds
are available

The otherwise satisfactory mitre fence slide supplied with the test machine was a poor fit in the bed grooves, but this problem has now been redressed; a replacement slide bar is available for those who own the early version.

The large aluminium casting body of the mitre guide bolts to a sliding fence, and can be easily set to any angle up to 60° each way; a drop through pin locates at the 0° and 45° settings.

Blade, speed changing

Undo a pair of clasp catches and the large door swings open, aided by a gas ram which operates like a CD ejecting from a stereo. Just why the door needs to open in this manner is a mystery – I've never had trouble opening machinery doors before, but the novelty of a self-opening one makes it worth having *(you sad man – Editor)*.

To replace the blade, hinge open the front of the sliding guard and loosen three ratchet levers under the bed to allow the fence bar to be swung to the right, out of the way.

Take the tension off the blade by turning the slightly too small knob on top of the machine, and remove the blade through the slot in the bed. Replace it with a fresh blade and re-tension it until the pointer on the max/min indicator is between two marks.

Blade tracking is controlled by another – too small – knob on the back of the machine. When the blade is running in the correct position the blade guide rollers can be set.

These are splendid examples of what blade guides should be, with purpose-made rollers tungsten-faced to take the unusual forces of a bandsaw blade. Their position on the blade is easy to set, although a screwdriver is required for the side guides.

It's good to see that the bottom set of guides is just as accessible as those at the top.

To select a different speed, a ratchet lever in the centre of the geared motor lifting knob is slackened; turn the knob to raise the motor, move the belt to the other pulley, re-tension and tighten the belt – easy!

Cutting

Raising and lowering the guard to suit the timber again works with a geared action operated by a large knob. Telescopic plates on the side of the blade guard ensure fingers are kept away from the blade at any setting.

The 3-phase motor I tested has bags of power and huge capacity; aided by the two speeds, the 15mm blade supplied as standard easily coped with huge lumps of wood without wander.

As with most bandsaws, a large range of blades is available.

Conclusion

After my initial suspicion at finding a bright red machine in the workshop I found the Cäsar to be well made and designed, with useful gearing features to aid almost all aspects of setting up.

The number of accessories available increases its potential, and at £1,170 including VAT for the basic machine it represents great value for money. ■

FACTS AND FIGURES

Price:	£1170 including VAT
Motor	Single phase 1.95kW (2.5hp)
	Three phase 2.3kW (3hp)
Table dimensions	608 by 608mm (24 by 24in)
Height of table	900mm (35½in)
Blade length	3430mm (135¹/₁₆)
Cutting height at 90°	300mm (12in)
Throat capacity	440mm (17³/₁₆in)
Capacity to fence	300mm (12in)
Table tilt	-20° to +45°
Blade speeds	463 and 776m/min (1519 and 2545ft/min)
Weight	190kg (418lb)

Available from: PRO Machine Tools Ltd, 17 Station Road Business Park, Barnack, Stamford, Lincs. PE9 3DW. Tel: 01780 740956/ Fax: 01780 740957

Sedgwick TA315

Technical Editor **Alan Goodsell** takes an exclusive look at Sedgwick's updated TA315 sawbench

F&C is the first magazine to get its hands on the uprated Sedgwick TA315. With the exception of the parallel fence – a scaled down version of the TA450's – on the surface it looks similar to the previous model, less noticeable differences being the larger, more substantial cabinet and a slightly larger bed.

It is, however, still compact for a machine of this calibre, and a tilting arbor and a sliding carriage are supplied as standard.

Construction

A nicely finished heavy gauge steel cabinet supports a well-machined cast-iron bed measuring 800mm (31$\frac{1}{2}$in) long by 755mm (29$\frac{3}{4}$in) wide.

The substantial steel bars for the sliding carriage and fence are firmly bolted to the bed, which has an aluminium gullet plate covering a large opening for changing the blade. The omission of a spindle lock makes blade changing difficult, requiring employment of the old method of jamming the blade with a block of wood.

To prepare for use, the machine needs only to be wired into the mains supply and the sliding carriage lifted into position; another pair of hands is useful here as it is cast-iron and rather heavy.

Cast aluminium is used for the crown guard; this has a blanked off 50mm (2in) extraction point that must be drilled out before it can be used with a dust extractor – I can't help feeling it wouldn't be too much trouble for this to be done at the factory, a blanking plate being supplied for when it isn't in use.

A useful feature of the crown guard is its ability to adjust its angle, allowing the blade to be kept high but retaining protection in front of it.

Blade height, angle

The arbor is mounted on a substantial steel arm mechanism designed for heavy duty use.

A large and well placed plastic wheel on the front

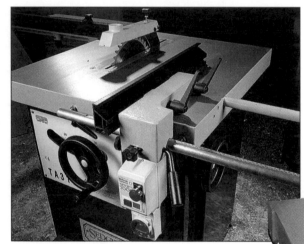

RIGHT: The new Sedgwick TA315

"There are no discernible stops for either position but the winding mechanism runs out of steam in just about the right place"

sawbench

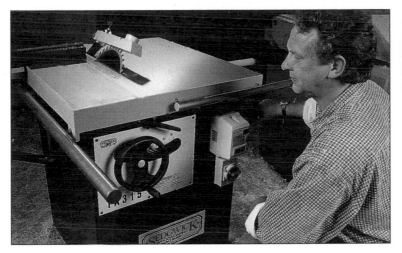

of the machine operates the rise-and-fall; its action is positive and well geared – even though slightly more effort is needed to wind it up than down.

The tilting action is also precise, with a range from 0° vertical to 45°; there are no discernible stops for either position but the winding mechanism runs out of steam in just about the right place. I hope this isn't just the end of the thread; if so then any debris collecting here will stop the tilt short of either 0° or 45°.

The locking lever needs only a small amount of movement to lock securely, which is just as well as it is placed in the small gap between the rise-and-fall wheel and the bed. A calibration gives a rough idea of the angle of the blade, although all angles will need checking before committing to a cut.

Parallel fence

A large cast-iron mounting bracket runs smoothly on a bar that protrudes beyond the bed by about 300mm (12in). Another bar sits behind it to support the fence when extended beyond the edge of the bed.

When fully extended it will give a ripping capacity of 610mm (24in) to the blade. Optional extension beds can be fitted to the end and side of the main bed, eliminating the need

for these protruding bars; without the extension beds in place, however, these sticking out bars have a habit of jabbing into the nether regions when manoeuvring around the machine – in common with most other woodworking machines.

The parallel fence is a meaty aluminium extrusion that can be slid back and forward on the mounting bracket to suit different types of sawing. As it can also be reversed it is convenient for sawing thick, thin or angled stock.

A long lever incorporating a cam device locks the fence in position. Although it doesn't need it, too much down pressure can easily be applied to the lever, resulting in the whole fence pivoting on the bar and lifting up.

The edge of the bracket lines up with a calibration on the bar and is quite accurate, but dust tends to accumulate in the corner making measurements difficult to read; more importantly there is no means of adjusting the zero point to allow for different blades or false fences.

For extra accuracy Sedgwick have included a well designed micro-adjuster. A knob on the front of the bracket locks the fence, and turning a knob on the side gives extremely precise movements.

When this new version fence is positioned and locked it is totally rigid – a major improvement on

their previous model and one from which many other machine manufacturers could learn a lesson or two.

Sliding carriage

The bed of the sliding carriage – another hefty piece of cast-iron – is supported at the inboard end on two huge rollers which move easily on the large diameter bar fixed to the main bed, with a third roller adjusted to take out any slack.

The outboard end is supported on a substantial cast arm that swings out of harm's way when the carriage is removed.

The crosscut fence is made from a substantial aluminium extrusion that is easily set to angles from 0° to 45°; adjustable stops at both of these extremities ensure accuracy, which is more than can be said for the quadrant calibration set into the bed. The markings on this don't line up with the fence when it is angled, although if a reading is taken from one end of the line it gives a rough guide to the fence angle.

The end of the fence extends to give a distance of 1900mm (74³/₄in) from the flimsy flipover stop to the blade; moving the sliding ➤

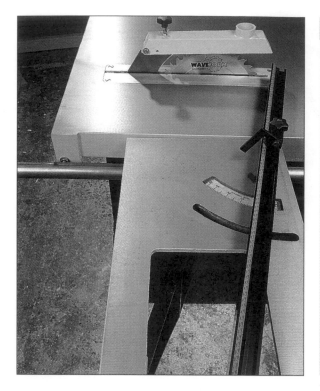

FACTS AND FIGURES

Motor	3kW
Blade diameter	310mm (12in)
Arbor size	30mm
Spindle speed	3700rpm
Blade projection at 0°	105mm (4$\frac{1}{8}$in)
Blade projection at 45°	76mm (3in)
Main bed size	800 x 755mm (31$\frac{1}{2}$in x 29$\frac{3}{4}$in)
Height of bed	850mm (33$\frac{1}{2}$in)
Sliding carriage bed size	600 x 350mm (24 x 13$\frac{3}{4}$in)
Distance saw to parallel fence	610mm (24in)
Distance saw to flipover stop	1900mm (74$\frac{3}{4}$in)
Maximum crosscut	600mm (23$\frac{5}{8}$in)

Prices:

Single phase 3.0kW	£1968 inc VAT
Three phase 3.0kW	£1909 inc VAT
R.H. extension table	£193 inc VAT*
Rear take-off table	£170 inc VAT*
Larger sliding carriage	£669 inc VAT*

*Plus £65 if not factory fitted

Contact : M. Sedgwick & Co. Ltd, Swinnow Lane, Leeds, LS13 4QG
tel 0113 2570637, fax 0113 2393412.

ABOVE:
Carriage's fence adjustable for angle... but exact settings cannot be made from the scale

carriage back provides a capacity of 600mm (23$\frac{5}{8}$in) between the fence and the blade.

This rigid and smooth rolling carriage is perfect for accurate crosscutting work, and for larger panel work a bigger sliding carriage is available as an extra.

In use

The simple and easy to use switchgear, including a padlockable isolating switch and an on/off switch, is well positioned on the front of the sawbench. A large red emergency off-button is placed so that a swift kick will stop the saw.

Dust doesn't present any more of a problem than on most sawbenches these days. The internal steel fabricated chute connects to an extractor via an outlet of 150mm (6in) diameter.

As mentioned before, if point-of-cut extraction is required the crown guard will need to be drilled first.

The single phase, 3kW motor is quite noisy but has plenty of

power, coping easily with a batch of 65mm (2$\frac{1}{2}$in) oak run through at a reasonable feed speed.

The sawbench is normally supplied with a general purpose blade but for the test I was supplied with a ripping blade.

There were no grumbles either, after running the sawbench on and off for most of the day while cutting a mixture of soft and hard woods for a kitchen project. The results were accurate and square.

Conclusion

Although similar in appearance to the previous model, the new TA315 is better in many ways, the fence and sliding carriage being built to standards that

should be emulated by other manufacturers, and the larger cabinet and bed being more robust.

It is ideal for a small joinery or furniture-making business that will put heavy demands on a machine that must be accurate.

The Sedgwick sawbench in its standard form is sturdy enough to cope with most types of work and, with a range of extension beds and larger sliding carriage available, its capabilities extend to large sheet material work. ■

SECOND OPINION

COLIN Eden-Eadon writes: I have used the predecessor of this model for a number of years and always found it to be reliable and accurate. The fences on this new version have been beefed up and are extremely solid, with no noticeable movement. The switchgear is more accessible and the accuracy of the sliding table is as good as it always has been. The Sedgwick is as solidly built as I would expect, and the mitre gauge is a useful guide on the sliding table, enabling mitres to be set up – but I would check them before cutting. This is a quality product with some useful improvements.

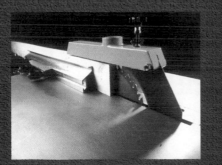

Stranger on the saw

MAIN PICTURE:
Emco Rex with
long sliding
carriage,
extension tables
and cabinet
base fitted –
very colourful

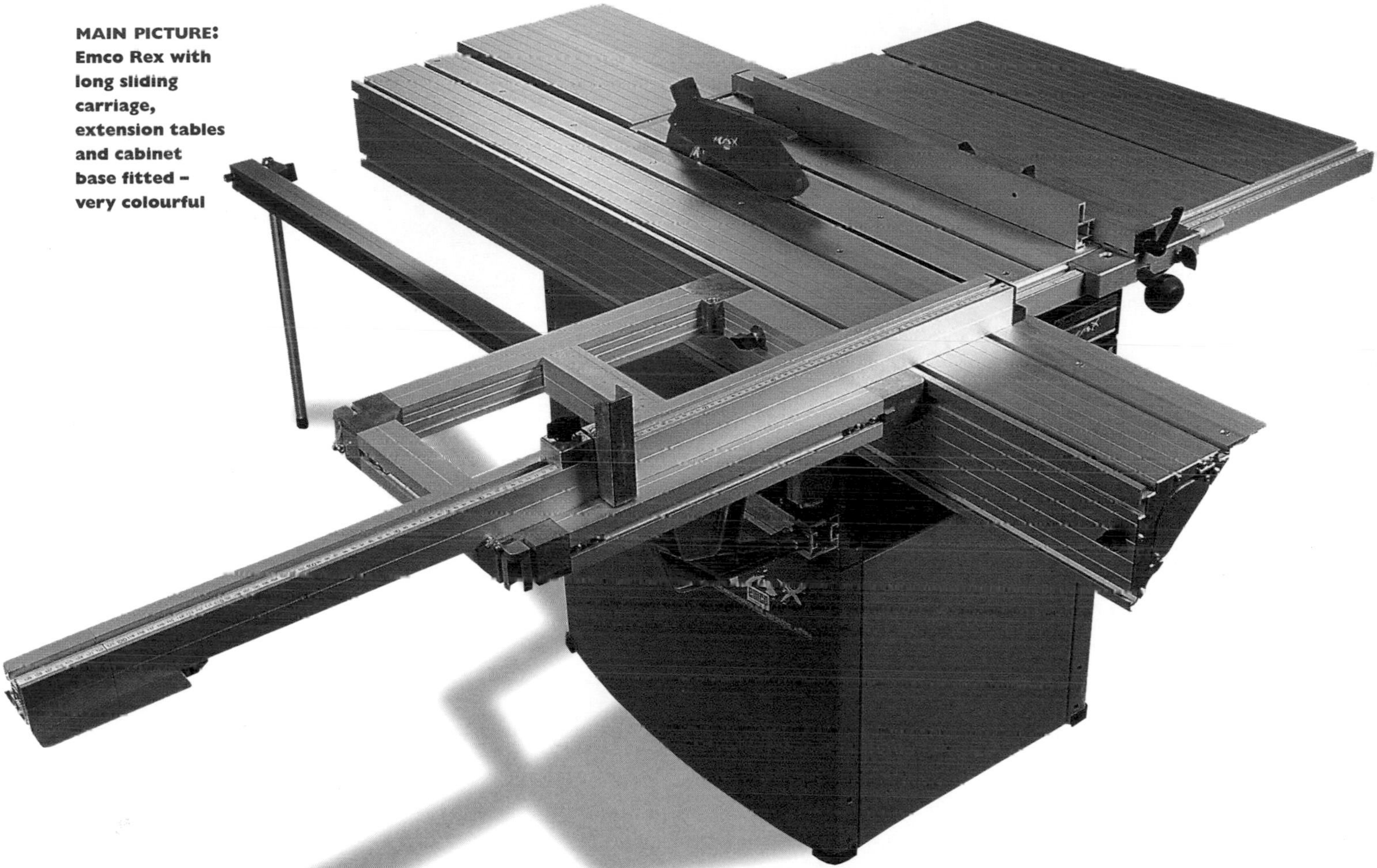

Anthony Bailey is tempted by the Emco Max table saw

"Please, Emco, let's have a proper, anglicised, translation – the leaflet provides more help!"

I ALWAYS ASSOCIATE the Austrian brand name Emco with small engineering lathes and milling machines. In fact, many woodworkers remember the Emco Rex multi-purpose woodworking machine with affection, and the demand for spares indicates many are still in use.

Emco has been a bit of a stranger in the UK of late, but they have never stopped making woodworking machinery; and now they are back to tempt furniture-makers with the Emco Max, a super-duper saw table with various add-ons.

System

The Max is a system rather than just a saw; this is not really what we're used to, but it makes some sense in that the newcomer can start with the basic saw then add extension tables, sliding carriage – even a scoring saw – as funds allow and the need arises, ending up with a panel saw of considerable capacity and refinement without the hassle of changing machines.

The heart of the system is a basic 250mm (10in) table saw, featuring a tilt-arbor and a bizarre cross-cutting feature which is activated by pulling a knob on the front of the casing. This knob turns out to be a handle which pulls the blade along the saw table – imagine a radial arm saw upside-down.

Although odd this is a proven approach, as the rarely-seen Elu table saw operates in the same way. This gives a cross-cutting capacity of 330mm (13in) as standard, which can be increased to 800mm (31½in) by adding a short sliding table or 1450mm (57in) with the long version tested here.

To support the large material sizes that this capacity allows, various table extensions are available and two machine stands are sold: an open frame type (the brochure says that this has logs – I think they mean legs) and a closed cabinet. The buyer can choose from several fences and stops, and for the clean cutting of faced sheet material a scoring saw can be added.

Construction

Typically for modern, lighter machines, the Max is a carefully designed and well manufactured construction of pressed steel and many aluminium extrusions, with a smattering of cast alloy – no cast iron to be found, of course.

All extrusions are substantial and accurately produced; likewise, the motor and the rest of the components are a testament to the care taken by Emco. The bright red livery is challenging, making a change from the rather tedious green in which most equipment is dressed.

The parts that make up this saw arrived in countless cardboard boxes, producing instant waste on a big scale. For putting them together the manual is unfortunately not very helpful, being in German with only small and obscure photos for guidance; please, Emco, let's have a proper, anglicised, translation – the brochure provides more information!

"Aluminium extrusions have a tendency to 'give' when a lot of pressure is applied, but everything stays straight and square once set up"

ABOVE: Cross-cut fence is lockable from 0° to 45°

BELOW: Without a sliding carriage the saw will cross-cut 330mm (13in), achieved by a pull-forward saw facility – note ➤ smart protractor

Sliding carriage

As you'd expect from a cross-cut table of this capacity it is quite large, the front end projecting sharply. The smooth-running sliding carriage can be locked with a pin if needed.

The cross-cut fence has a

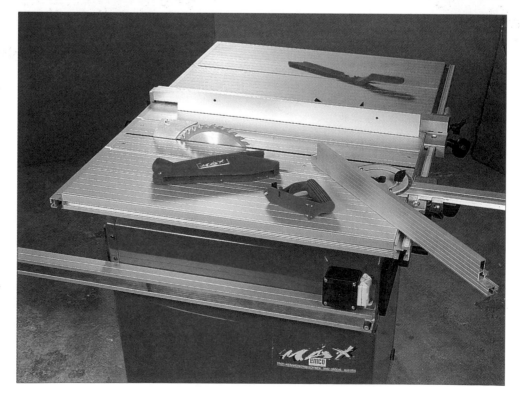

ABOVE RIGHT:
Fine adjustment
and scale magnifier
on rip fence

BELOW RIGHT:
Well-placed
controls, but on-
switch obscuring
cover not helpful

positive flip-over stop with a scale magnifier; it can be locked at any angle up to 45° ensuring that cutting mitres, including compound angles by using the tilt arbor as well, is very easy. Usefully the tilt arbor covers a range from -2° to 47° and is operated by a pull-out pin under the front-mounted rise-and-fall handwheel. Both these adjustments work smoothly.

Rip fence

The rip fence has fine adjustment and a scale magnifier; however, once the adjustment is twiddled and the fence is locked tight, its back end tends to swing across to its locked position – so check the blade to fence distance independently.

Once set the fence is rigid, and can be adjusted for rip- or panel-cutting.

On test

The motor is powerful, relatively quiet and well balanced, working with the 48-tooth TCT laser-cut saw blade to produce a quick and very easy cut with an impressive, almost planed finish.

Aluminium extrusions have a tendency to 'give' when a lot of pressure is applied, but everything stays straight and square once set up. The sharp corners of the extrusions bothered me though; I would take a file to them if I owned this saw. The safety pattern switch has a lift-up cover which hides the on-button; this is bit of a nuisance.

The job of a table saw is to make straight cuts in solid wood and sheet material; a dimension saw has to produce accurate cross-cuts and, preferably, be adjustable for angle. The Emco does all of these reliably and, as already mentioned, build quality is high.

Conclusion

With a base price of £888 including VAT for the basic table saw this may not be a cheap machine, but it is very well made. The expandability of the system is probably the factor which will affect most people's decision, and there are few alternatives – who else offers a choice of two sliding carriages?

So if you plan to start small with the option of increasing capacity later, or want to make up your ideal saw from the various options, then the Emco is well worth a look.

FACTS AND FIGURES

Manufacturer	Emco Maier (Austria)
Maximum cut height	83mm (3¼in)
Blade diameter	250mm (10in)
Cut height at 45°	55mm (2in)
Motor power	2.85hp (1ph*)
Table size (basic)	345 x 810mm
	(13½ x 32in)
Weight	100kg

*3ph model available

● Price examples, all including VAT:

Saw table	£888
Sliding table 1450mm (57in)	£351
Fence	£97.50
R/h table extension	£129
Scoring saw	£232

● Availability: contact PRO Machine Tools Ltd, 17 Station Road Business Park, Barnack, Stamford, Lincs, tel 01780 740956, fax 01780 740957.

Robland ZX 30 t

In the search for a cast-iron cabinetmaker's table saw at a reasonable price, F&C unearthed this 10in example. **Colin Eden-Eadon** rather liked it…

PHOTOGRAPHY BY CHRIS SKARBON

IN a previous issue of F&C our Editor bemoaned the fact that nobody now makes a cast-iron 10in saw of good quality that is both compact and affordable for the small maker.

This drove him to buy a Startrite TA 175 but, had he seen this Robland, he might have saved himself the trouble.

The Belgian Robland company has a long track record of producing high quality woodworking machinery and I have always had a secret hankering after one of their famous combination machines. So it was with some excitement that I looked forward to testing the Robland ZX 30

table saw, which is part of the family of machines that includes the more well-known combination machine, the LX 310 *(tested on page 64)*.

For some time the Robland range of machines was badged and sold by Startrite, who are also well-known for their fine bandsaws and other machines, but in recent years Startrite and Robland have parted company, and Startrite is now a part of the Record group of companies. Robland machines are now available from Wilson Brothers.

Construction

The ZX 30 is very solidly built,

as I expected from this manufacturer, with cast-iron table and sliding carriage.

The tables are supported by a heavy gauge fabricated steel casing. An extension table, also of fabricated steel, wraps around the main saw table in an L shape, supported on a substantial bracket and arms of almost RSJ proportions.

Although the saw is made of some serious metal, I found it was quite easy to move around.

The machine arrived already set up. The blade, riving knife and crown guard were all retracted below the table, just

able saw

requiring the table insert to be removed in order to wind the assembly up into operating position.

This example came supplied with the largest steel extension table fitted; this increases its width from 445mm to 800mm and its length from 800m to 1,323mm.

The larger of two available sliding carriages was fitted, which means that the whole thing takes up quite a lot of room in the workshop.

However, the sliding carriage assembly is easily removed to liberate some extra workshop space when needed; the table is released from the carriage by the removal of a cotter pin, the carriage itself by undoing two handles, one at each end .

Rise-and-fall

The rise-and-fall is effected by means of a pull-and-push lever, as opposed to the more usual wind-up and -down variety, but I did not find this a problem as it is very precise. A very positive locking mechanism for this works by a clockwise turn of its handle, and very little movement is needed to adjust the depth of cut.

The Robland's rip fence is the familiar aluminium extrusion that seems to be the norm these days; it works well, though, with no noticeable play, and can be adjusted for parallel with two Allen bolts.

The fence runs along a rectangular section bar and has no fine adjuster, but for precise work I always set up to a steel rule anyway, so for me this not a problem.

Electrics

This saw is available in both single- and three-phase versions.

The manual is very clear on wiring, which is commendably straightforward. Although it also serves as the manual for several other machines in the range, and the English being a little clipped, it has very clearly presented drawings and is understandable. I have seen much worse in my time, including some from British manufacturers!

The electrics for the switches are well protected in a hinged box; as well as an isolating switch, two stop buttons are provided – one to the operator's front and one with the start button, which is in a curious position on the side of the switch box.

It is possible to reach round from the front of the saw to switch on, but this means leaning back over an already-running saw. I became used to walking round to the switch; again not really a problem, just a little idiosyncratic.

Sliding carriage

To my mind, this is what makes this saw stand out from the pack.

By undoing two handles, one at the front and another at the back, the carriage's guide rail can be slid back or forward; when

fully back, a 1290mm (4ft 2¾in) width board can be cross-cut. A solid steel leg is provided to add extra stability when the rail is at its full extent.

ABOVE: Solid, RSJ-like extension table support

"The sliding carriage makes this saw stand out from the pack"

The cross-cut table remains in place during this adjustment, a well thought-out piece of design. Once board cutting is finished, the guide rail can be slid back into its normal position, again releasing valuable workshop space.

The table itself is cast-iron and as solid as the main table. The guide rail consists of two stainless steel bars with an aluminium ➤

BELOW: Ripping at an angle, note crown guard extraction

FACTS AND FIGURES

Price	£1,748 including VAT
RPM	4000
Motor single phase	3hp
Motor three phase	3 or 4hpz
Saw table size	800 x 445mm (31½ x 17¾in)
With extension and carriage	1,323 x 800 mm (4ft 4in x 31½in)
Maximum blade diameter	250mm (10in)
Bore of shaft	30mm
Max. depth of cut at 90°	85mm (3⅜in)
Max. depth of cut at 45°	55mm (2⅛in)
Max. saw stroke cross cut	1290mm (4ft 2¾in)
Max. parallel cut	660mm (26in)
Weight	235kg

● Contact: Wilson Brothers at Head Office, Springhead Enterprise Park, Springhead Road, Northfleet, Kent DA11 8HL, tel 01474 561414, fax 01474 561515.

extrusion between them; the table then runs on bearings sitting on the two bars.

This arrangement allows for very smooth running, and when cutting sheet material it proved to be very accurate with no discernible play or run-out.

An aluminium cross-cut fence is attached to the table via a steel post with a collar and wing nuts; these nuts are a little awkward to tighten when adjusting the fence. Also fitting to the steel post is a nice solid toggle clamp.

A fairly run-of-the-mill mitre fence is supplied with the saw, but this is hardly needed except for small work, as the cross-cut fence can be set to any angle.

Extraction is well thought-out and comes with all the necessary bits, including a fitting and hose for the extraction outlet on the well-made crown guard.

In use

Motor power is 3hp on this single-phase version, so there is plenty of oomph for sawing. Three-phase users get to choose between 3 and 4hp motors.

Because of the good solid table and substantial base there is no movement and little vibration of the saw when operating, floor-mounting points are provided for fixing if required and, if you prefer, a wheeled carriage is available at extra cost for super-easy moving around.

I ran some 50mm (2in) softwood and various sizes of mixed hardwoods through the saw with no trouble at all, even when cutting some maple, which is very tough stuff! The ample extension table allows for safer sawing by providing a good run-off area. The tilt arbor works well up to its full 45°, operated by a cranked lever on the machine's side.

Blade changing is made very easy by provision of a ring spanner with cut-out notches – these locate on the blade collar – and a bar which locks the arbor through a hole in the saw table.

"The Robland looked so nice in Colin's workshop that he bought it"

Conclusion

The whole set up is very accurate and has a professional and solid feel to it, capable of achieving fine work as well as coping with heavier ripping and cross-cutting of solid timber and sheet material.

This is a nicely thought-out and adaptable saw, built to a high standard of engineering. Moreover, its price is attractive when compared to other machines on the market with similar specification; consider the cast-iron tables, large table extension as standard, huge and steady cross-cutting capacity – you get a lot for your money.

I liked this saw a lot, and it would be at the top of my test-drive list for both the serious amateur and professional furniture-maker. My only quibble is that it would be nice to see some more solid fences; the aluminium ones fitted are accurate, but in an ideal world...

TOP: Cutting a mitre using the sliding carriage and substantial toggle clamp

ABOVE: Clever design enables sliding carriage to be extended simply by undoing two handles, one at each end

BELOW: Guide bars fully extended with support leg allowing 1290mm cross-cutting capacity

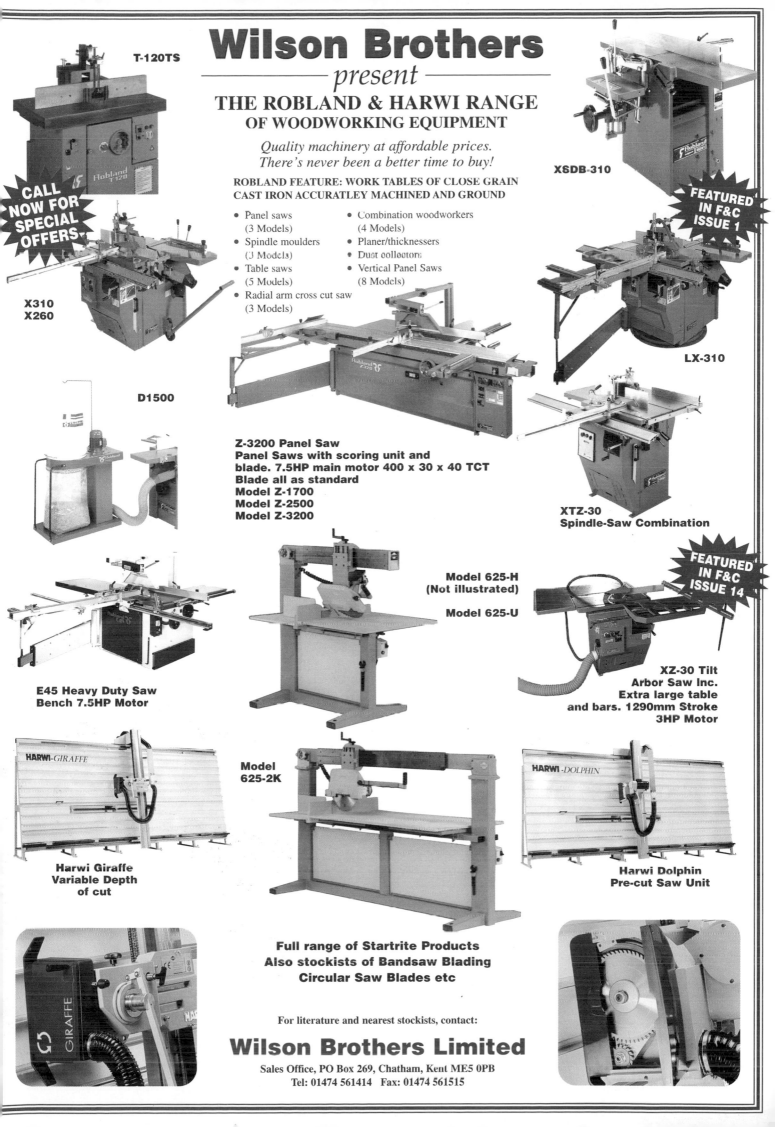

MiniMax SC3

Technical Editor **Alan Goodsell** is hard put to find fault with the MiniMax SC3 sawbench

SCM have used their talent for spotting quality woodworking machines to become the main distributors in the UK of the MiniMax range from Italy.

Sawbenches being the starting point in processing wood, finding one that will suit individual requirements is crucial.

This one from MiniMax, available in either single or three-phase, was described to me by Brian Stacey of SCM as the machine that persuaded him to join their ranks.

While it is aimed at those who are involved with sawing quantities of sheet material, its construction will easily cope with some hefty plank sawing.

CE regulations are easily complied with, and the sawbench comes with a 12-month electrical/mechanical warranty.

Construction

The SC3 is a solid, robust machine boasting a heavy cast-iron bed and a long 2300 by 230mm (90^1/$_2$ by 9in) fabricated steel sliding bed. With the main bed, it sits on top of a sturdy sheet-steel cabinet.

A box section steel open frame clamps to the sliding bed, the other end being supported on a heavy duty two-part arm that scissors conveniently out of the operator's way when the bed is pushed forward.

The machine is largely assembled when delivered, with only

the extension beds and fences to bolt on. Enough tools are supplied to both assemble the sawbench and set it up.

A comprehensive operating manual — which confusingly makes some references to other models — is supplied. The useful parts manual has large, clear breakdown drawings of every component.

> "The action of rise-and-fall is silky smooth; although there is no locking device it happily stays where it is set"

Setting up

A 250mm blade, if not already in place, will need fitting. It is easily mounted on the 30mm arbor through a trapdoor on the side of the machine, after sliding off a cover on the dust extractor collector. A larger 300mm blade can be fitted if the scoring attachment is removed.

The main blade must be of the same kerf thickness as the scoring blade; I fitted one of my own, but SCM will supply a blade to suit the purchaser's needs.

The action of rise-and-fall is silky smooth; although there is no locking device it happily stays where it is set. A good quality plastic handwheel is utilised for both the rise-and-fall and the tilt — which operates just as smoothly.

A calibration on the front is a useful guide for setting the blade angle, its accuracy confirmed when a test piece is run through the saw.

A positive stop for 0° vertical and 45° is securely locked to the

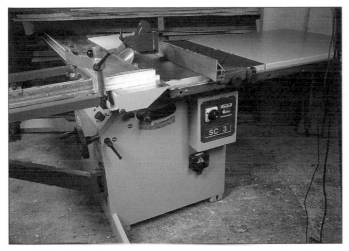

ABOVE: Operator's eye view — everything neatly to hand, all works smoothly

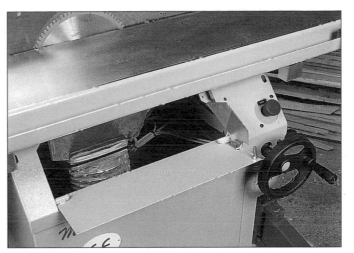

ABOVE: Changing the blade entails opening this trap door and sliding the extraction gubbins out of the way — a bit of a trial

desired angle with a plastic ratchet lever.

The SC3 is a machine ideal for sawing faced material as it has a scoring saw attachment supplied as standard. Unusually this attachment can be adjusted for height independently of the main saw blade.

Sliding carriage

A steel bar slung underneath the long sliding bed runs smoothly on bearings. These are adjustable to take up extraneous movement; further bearings support the sliding bed adjacent to the main bed.

Located under the operator's end of the machine is a handle which locks the sliding bed in position. This feature comes into its own when manhandling large pieces of slithery material.

The open frame table clamps to a trough running along the side of the sliding bed. The table frame can be secured in any position along the bed to accommodate the dimensions of the current task.

"Clever spring-loaded stops enable two cutting dimensions to be set"

This frame is rigid and is suited to larger panels, smaller stock tending to fall through it.

Fully extending the sliding bed's supporting arm allows a maximum cutting capacity in front of the scoring saw of 1200mm (47^1/4in).

The aluminium extruded fence is easy to set at any angle from 0° to 45°. A wooden tip provides support for stock close to the blade and also acts as a chipbreaker. The fence can be extended to give a cutting capacity of 2300mm (90^1/2in) to the left of the blade; clever spring-loaded stops enable two cutting dimensions to be set

at any one time.

A substantial, cam-operated hold-down clamp secures the work fairly close to the blade, owing to the bed construction.

Bolting a strange little foot to the base of the cabinet counteracts the possibility of the machine tipping over if a long, heavy board upsets its balance — bolting the sawbench to the floor would also work.

Extending beds

A bolt-on sheet-steel bed extends the length of the main bed from 835mm (32^7/8in) to 1380mm (54^1/4in). Although it's only fixed at one end, it seems to give enough support for panel work.

A 940mm (37in) side extension bed bolts to the main bed; a rather flimsy box section leg supports the other side. Extra rigidity for the bed is provided by the parallel fence's box section mounting bar that also bolts to the main bed.

Both the extension beds are painted, a finish which I suspect will wear off after heavy use.

The parallel fence's mounting bracket is a substantial casting which slides smoothly on its bar. The accurate calibration on the bar has a double-sided pointer for precise measuring with the aluminium fence in either the upright or level position.

The fence at maximum stretch over the extension bed gives a full sheet width cutting capacity of 1270mm (50in). A well made micro adjuster on the fence bracket works well, and ensures

Price	£2,784 including VAT
Motor	1.8kW (2.5hp) single phase
Maximum blade dia. without scorer	300mm (12in)
Maximum blade dia. with scorer	250mm (10in)
Depth of cut with 300mm blade	100mm (4in)
Depth of cut with 250mm blade	75mm (3in)
Main blade arbor	30mm
Main blade speed	4000rpm
Scoring blade speed	8000rpm
Main bed size	560 by 840mm (22 by 33in)
Sliding table size	2300 by 230mm (90½ by 9in)
Maximum width of cut to parallel fence	1270mm (50in)
Maximum width of cut to left of blade	2300mm (90½in)
Capacity from scorer blade to sliding carriage fence	1200mm (47¼in)

> "Bolting a strange little foot to the base of the cabinet counteracts the possibility of the machine tipping over if a long, heavy board upsets its balance"

RIGHT: The scoring saw blade is adjustable for height through an Allen key access hole — a useful feature

precise, fine adjustments to the cutting width.

In use

The 1.8kW (2.5hp) motor runs quietly as well as being quite gentle on the power supply at start-up. It has plenty of power and copes well with thick sheet material and solid wood.

Large extension beds and long sliding bed make life easier when support for sheet material is required.

A combination of the large fence bracket and rigid fences ensures good accuracy of cut and quick setting.

The scoring blade left a clean cut on the underside of all the types of material tried, whether MFC, veneered MDF or solid wood, and this example has the advantage of being independently adjustable for height.

Extraction is arranged with neat internal pipework to a 120mm ($4^3/4$in) outlet on the end of the machine, with a further outlet on the crown guard. When linked into the workshop extraction system, dust from the sawbench was kept to a minimum.

Switches

The control switches are placed to hand on the front right-hand side of the sawbench; they include a rotating, isolating switch and small, sealed on and off push buttons. A large emergency off button is placed conveniently near at hand on the left. The sawbench must be permanently wired into a mains supply.

Conclusion

The MiniMax sawbench is a sturdy workhorse that I found difficult to fault.

It has the capacity for cutting

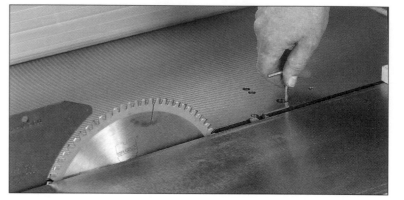

full sheets of material and is strong enough for prolonged, heavy workshop use.

Fully extended, it requires a large workshop and, with both extension beds fitted, the SC3 needs a space of 3440mm wide by 3620 long ($135^1/2$ by $142\ ^1/2$in) in which to fit just the machine, before operating space is considered.

Given the need for a machine like this, and the space in which to run it, the SC3 should be high up on the list for a test drive.

Contact: SCM GB, Dabell Avenue, Blenheim Industrial Estate, Bulwell, Nottingham NG8 8WA, tel 0115 977 0044, fax 0115 977 0946.

ABOVE: An impressive saw — if you have the space for it

"I found the old and trusted eyeball method to be the most reliable"

Scheppach ts4010

Technical Editor **Alan Goodsell** tries out the revamped

Scheppach ts 4010

SCHEPPACH ARE renowned for producing a large range of versatile woodworking machines, aimed at the small workshop.

The ts 4010 – the latest incarnation of their flagship sawbench – displays more features than its predecessor. Those needing a machine that will cope well with most aspects of sawing will not be disappointed with the enhanced Scheppach.

Whereas some other manufacturers' accounts departments seem to be involved in devising economies disguised as improvements, Scheppach has come up with a machine that is actually an improvement on the old.

Construction

This machine has the distinctive Scheppach mix of heavy gauge steel for the fabricated cabinet and good quality extruded aluminium for the beds and fences.

Expect to spend at least a day putting the machine together and setting it up, even with the assistance of the usual ambiguously translated multi-lingual manuals; exploded component drawings provide the most help.

Spanners supplied with the machine are for setting-up rather than assembly, but Scheppach should provide a few cheap spanners for this task to save the user having to hunt round in a spartan workshop spanner box.

Setting-up

A dual purpose wheel for rise-and-fall and tilt is conveniently placed on the front of the machine, facing the operator.

Although the rise-and-fall cannot be locked into position, I experienced no unwanted movement once a particular depth of cut was set – even under heavy use.

Tilt action is also smooth and precise, and requires the wheel to be pulled out and engaged into tilt mode. With a spring-loaded return, a constant pulling pressure has to be applied while setting an angle.

The tilt action is fast, only a few turns of the wheel moving the blade from vertical to 45°, but not so fast that it impairs ➤

"Once put together and switched on, this neat little unit proved to be quiet and to have an impressive amount of suck"

ABOVE: Handwheel operated rise-and-fall and tilt adjustment is within easy reach, as is the switchgear

accuracy required for setting-up. Unlike the rise-and-fall, the tilt has a lock; a stop makes a return to vertical easy.

A visually complicated scale on the front indicates the angle of blade and depth of cut, but I found the old and trusted eyeball method to be the most reliable.

The fence bracket slides on a bar on the front of the machine. Taking a reading from the calibration on the bar by sighting through the fence bracket lens proved surprisingly accurate.

Flip-down levers lock the fence firmly in the set position. Fine adjustments to the width of cut can then be made with a built-in micro-adjuster, sited on the left-hand side of the bracket.

The L-shaped aluminium part of the ripping fence can be rotated to make the sawing of thin stock easier; with the fence in this position a different calibration on the mounting bar is used.

Two large inserts either side of the blade are easily removed to afford good access to the arbor

BELOW: 300mm blade gives good ripping capacity – note also the useful run-off table

when blade changing. With the blade in the upright position, the shaft is locked by inserting a tommy-bar through the bed to engage in a hole in the drive pulley.

Electrics

The ts 4010 has a two pin European socket fitted; an appropriate plug is supplied ready to be wired into a mains cable. This makes wiring up easy as the job can be done at a convenient level rather than having to grovel about on the floor trying to peer into a dark electrical box.

The drawback is that unless the wire is clipped out of harm's way it can easily be tripped over and the plug pulled from its socket.

An isolator switch is mounted on exactly the opposite side of the machine to the conveniently placed on/off switch. This means a walk round the saw to make the machine safe for setting-up.

Sawing

The combination of a powerful 2.2kW, 3hp motor and the standard 315mm, 12in blade on the single-phase machine I tested provides bags of power to saw large capacity stock. A three-phase version is also available.

I ran some 40mm, $1^1/2$in softwood and hardwood through the saw, and couldn't get the blade to slow unless extreme pressure was applied to the stock.

The high pitched whistle that emanates from the blade ensures the need to wear ear defenders, but this shouldn't be a hardship as they should be close to hand anyway, to prevent permanent aural damage from all the other high-frequency workshop noises.

The saw produces little vibration, and what there is is further reduced by rubberised feet fitted to the base. These feet, coupled with the light weight of the machine, make sliding the sawbench to a new position easy, but unfortunately this also tends to happen when sawing. A lifting wheel base is available for moving the machine around even more easily.

Scheppach claim a splinter-free cut with a planed finish; although I found the quality of cut to be very good there is still some spelching on the underside of cut stock.

To further improve the cut and eliminate break-out on solid timber and faced materials, an

inexpensive scoring saw accessory can be obtained. Although this limits the size of the main blade to 250mm, 10in it is quickly fitted or removed, so changing to a larger blade for ripping is not inconvenient.

Sliding carriage

The sliding carriage is another assembly that can be quickly fitted or removed from the machine – a bonus which makes the lengthy process of initial assembly and setting it up worthwhile.

The carriage is built up from more good quality aluminium extrusions and sheet-steel.

The large bed and long travel of the carriage proved useful for dimensioning sheet material, providing excellent cross-cutting capacity. The carriage rail can be slid back to provide a huge capacity of 1300mm, 51in in front of the blade and, with the fence fully extended, dimensioning up to 1750mm, 69in from blade to stop is possible.

The substantial fence is unfussy and quick to set at any angle between 0° and 45° either way. An ingenious plunging stop returns the fence to 0°, and all other angles are accurately set using the large, easy to read calibration.

No hold-down clamp is supplied, but a hole in the fence would take one although none is listed as an extra.

A nicely made flip-over stop fits either the sliding carriage fence or the slightly less accurate sawbench mitre fence. The stop has a good micro-adjuster for accurate adjustments when setting-up.

The sliding action of the carriage is very smooth and precise, but with quite a lot of movement when weight is put on the outer edge of the carriage bed. For short stock this wouldn't be a problem but inaccuracies will creep in when using longer, heavier pieces of wood.

An 800mm, $31^1/2$in long, aluminium outfeed table provides useful support. This clips onto brackets bolted to the end of the saw and is easily fitted and removed, a single flip-down leg giving enough support.

Extraction

Among the plethora of boxes that Scheppach sent I found their HA 2600 dust extractor.

This involved another lengthy assembly job, but once put together and switched on, this neat little unit proved to be quiet and to have an impressive amount of suck.

It coped easily with the waste from the well plumbed sawbench, both from the main outlet and the top of the crown-guard. The small dust bag would need changing frequently with general workshop use, but is ideally suited to low-volume fine dust from a saw.

A typical cloth filtration bag is supplied as standard, but a more efficient filter cartridge can be obtained which looks as if it has been pinched from a truck's air-filter box.

Because static electricity can build up in plastic extractor pipes, a number of earth wires with crocodile clips on the end are supplied. These should be clipped between the various metal parts, including the wire that runs through the flexible pipe which is then earthed to the sawbench.

Another handy extra is an automatic switch-on mechanism. Both the extractor and the sawbench are plugged into it, so when the saw is fired-up the extractor starts at the same time.

Conclusion

The ts 4010 is a well made and thought out machine and is ideal for those with precision sawing requirements – especially using sheet material.

It has plenty of power and will

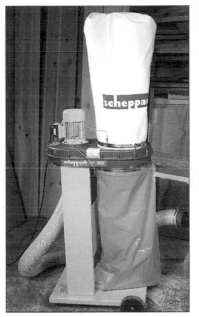

ABOVE: HA 2600 dust extractor is a good performer – shown here with standard cloth filter bag, cartridge filter further improves efficiency

have no problem coping with large capacity work. I have some reservations about the durability of aluminium extruded beds in a commercial workshop, where large rough-sawn boards are likely to be slapped down onto them.

If treated with care, though, the Scheppach should serve its owner well – it is a versatile, precision machine. Its capabilities are further enhanced by the large numbers of accessories available. ∎

FACTS AND FIGURES

Scheppach ts 4010 sawbench, single-phase

Price ....£1,208 including VAT
Bed size ....800 x 680mm, 31$\frac{1}{2}$ x 27in
Bed height ....850mm, 33$\frac{1}{2}$in
Maximum blade diameter 315mm, 12in
Cutting depth at 90° ....107mm, 4$\frac{1}{4}$in
Cutting depth at 45° 74mm, 3in
Maximum parallel cut............390mm, 15$\frac{3}{8}$in
Motor 2.2kW, 3hp
Speed...4,000rpm
Weight 125kg, 275lb

Scoring saw attachment
Price ....£112 including VAT
Blade diameter................................80mm, 3in

Sliding carriage
Price ....£398 including VAT
Bed size ....500 x 480mm, 19$\frac{3}{4}$ x 19in
Rail length ....2000mm, 78$\frac{3}{4}$in
Weight 37kg, 81lb

Bed length extension
Price ....£185 including VAT
Bed size.................800 x 480mm, 31$\frac{1}{2}$ x 19in

Lifting wheel base
Price ....£94 including VAT

Dust extractor HA 2600
Price ....£615 including VAT
Filter cartridge price........£109 including VAT
Bag capacity ....80 litres
Hose diameter 100mm, 4in
Weight 31.5kg

Automatic switch-on mechanism
Price ....£85 including VAT

Contact:
Scheppach
(Tel: 01484 531446)

ABOVE: Squaring up panels made easy with the sliding carriage

ABOVE: ts 4010 with sliding carriage added, giving a huge 1300mm cross-cutting capacity

MiniMax T40i

Technical Editor **Alan Goodsell** puts the Minimax spindle moulder, now reintroduced to the UK by SCM, under his lens

PHOTOGRAPHY BY
ANTHONY BAILEY

FAR RIGHT: No gimmicky speed indicators – just a window in front of the drive

NOTTINGHAM-BASED company SCM now import the extensive range of Italian-made MiniMax woodworking machines. The T 40i is their top of the range spindle moulder.

It boasts features including a tilting arbor for increasing the capabilities of the machine, an optional sliding carriage and a powerful 3hp, 2.2kW motor. A three-phase version is available, as is a fixed spindle version, the T40.

Unfortunately the sliding carriage wasn't available for our test, but I did have a chance to inspect one at the 'Woodmex' show and can confirm that it is as rigid and well-built as the spindle moulder to which it belongs.

Construction

Make sure there is a fork lift, or a group of strong mates, available to lift the hefty 300kg, 660lb machine into place. It is delivered shrink-wrapped, fully assembled apart from the sliding carriage.

RIGHT: Unusual tilting spindle opens up new possibilities

The weight of the machine is mainly due to the large cast-iron bed that sits on a heavy gauge fabricated steel cabinet, with added mass supplied by a couple of large concrete blocks inside.

In spite of all this the machine slid around on a smooth concrete floor with surprising ease. As with all static machines it should be bolted to the floor.

Three aluminium rings are set in to the cast-iron bed to support short stock, and a centre plug fills the hole when the spindle is wound down.

With the fences removed, the bed becomes a solid, flat work surface – I often use my spindle bed as a supplementary assembly bench.

The manual is multi lingual and a little vague, but it has the saving grace of superb illustrations. The parts book is also well illustrated and gives all the information on the T40i's construction that could be required.

Tilting spindle

The 30mm diameter spindle can be tilted from 0° vertical to 45° forward, *see picture*, invaluable for setting up tricky cutter angles. This facility gives cutters a new angle of attack, to create mouldings that would be difficult to achieve with a fixed spindle. It also eliminates the dangers involved when some operators foolishly place cutters at extreme angles in a cutter block – often held in place only by a prayer.

The cutter blocks are bolted to the spindle through a bull-nosed collar, on either side of which Allen keys are tightened into keyways milled into the spindle. This works well enough and holds the block securely, but it seems a bit fussy compared to the simple system of a large nut on top of the spindle, found on most other machines and used for years.

A fairly limited selection of spacing collars is supplied; a larger range to accommodate the huge variation of blocks available would be useful, and would also give more scope for gapping tenoning discs.

Confusion of levers

Winding a large, removable plastic wheel on the front of the machine operates the tilting action; make sure that both the locking levers are slackened first – one is on the left of the machine and the other on the right.

The positioning of the levers caused some confusion at first; it was assumed the calibrated lever was the only one, and I wondered why the tilt action was so stiff. Once both are loosened, the tilt action is smooth and precise,

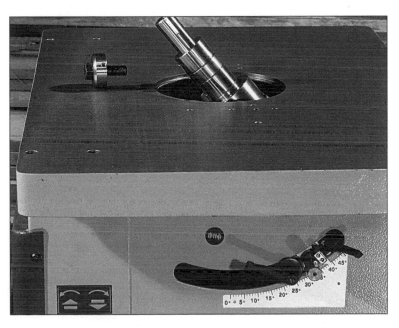

"Years of spindle use has trained me never to put my hands near the cutter block after pressing the switch, yet this is precisely what you have to do here"

with a positive stop at 0° to ensure the spindle returns accurately to vertical.

When the spindle is tilted the motor swings into an otherwise empty 'box' in the back of the machine's case. On top of this is a rubber mat, a useful place for spanners and tools when setting up – they should be removed before starting machining, though.

The plastic wheel for the tilt is also used for the rise-and-fall. Once slipped onto the shaft, the winding action is as smooth as the tilt, and is well geared for fine adjustments. Tucked behind the wheel, the locking lever is rather small and a bit inaccessible, but it locks the rise-and-fall firmly.

Controls and switches

All the controls and levers are placed so they are easy to reach, the switchgear is to hand on the front of the machine. Four switches are fitted; a large, locking-off button, a padlockable isolating switch, a start button and a three-position selector switch.

Why does a single function machine need a selector switch? Because it incorporates a function for releasing the brake that I consider to be extremely unnerving at the very least. This is how it works.

To start the machine, the selector switch is rotated from centre-off to the right, then the on-button is pressed, starting the motor.

To disable the electric brake, the selector switch is rotated from centre-off to the left, then the on-button is pressed, releasing the brake.

Not much difference, is there? Years of spindle use has trained me never to put my hands near the cutter block after pressing the switch, yet this is precisely what you have to do here. The consequences of turning the switch to

the right instead of left would be messy.

If the correct procedure is followed it is quite safe, but I feel that a separate switch would reduce the potential for a simple, catastrophic mistake to be made.

Hoods and fences

The hood is a robust aluminium casting with good quality plywood cheeks on the fences.

The left-hand fence has a micro-adjuster to create an offset between the two fences. It is precise and, although a sharp tap to release it was required, the action is pleasantly smooth. A crude calibration doesn't

do justice to the rest of the assembly.

The Shaw guard assembly is the most robust I have seen in a while, the main part being made from heavy gauge pressed steel with a hexagonal steel bar to support the well made guards. When fully extended they will accommodate timber capacities of up to 140 by 110mm, $5^1/_2$ by $4^3/_8$in. The whole unit lifts up to give good access to the cutter block but the plastic knobs, although large enough, could do with finger indents for better grip.

The familiar-looking ring ➤

MiniMax T40i spindle moulder in full cry

FACTS AND FIGURES

Price: T 40i tilting spindle	£2261 including VAT
Table size	560 x 870mm, 22 x 34¹/₄in
Spindle speeds	1,400, 3,000, 6,000, 8,000rpm
Spindle dia	30mm
Spindle tilt	0° to 45°
Motor	2.2kW, 3hp
Weight	300kg, 660lb
Price: Sliding carriage	£593 inc. VAT
Table size	628 x 430mm, in
Stroke to cutter	860mm, 33⁷/₈in
Weight	276kg, 608lbs

Prices are for single-phase, and ex-works from Nottingham.

For information contact SCM GB. Dabell Avenue, Blenheim Industrial Estate, Bulwell, Nottingham NG8 8WA.
Tel 0115 977 0044, fax: 0115 977 0946.

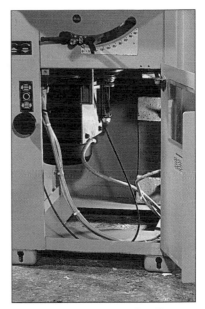

ABOVE: Plenty of room for the motor to swing when the spindle is tilted

ABOVE: Nicely made ring fence

"The self-braking motor stopped the Omas tiger-head cutter block in just over two seconds"

fence and hood unit is well made and easy to bolt to the bed – although it sits at a strange angle.

There is some give in the ring when extended from the mounting bracket; light, profile work wouldn't move it but a heavy jig might.

In use

When running, the T 40i is extremely quiet and vibration-free. The 3hp, 2.2kW motor supplies heaps of power through all of the four speeds and happily ran out the mouldings on a pile of mahogany (*Swietania macrophylla*) window components.

The self-braking motor stopped the Omas tiger-head cutter block in just over two seconds; a slight initial delay, then the brake bites in fast.

Access for speed-changing through a large door on the right-hand side is good. The motor is slackened and the 'v'-belt moved to the required pulley – sitting on the floor helps.

Many woodworking machines have an awkward to position gadget linking the pulley position to a speed indicator on the exterior of the machine; the T 40i has a more efficient and less complicated system for viewing speeds – a window in the door!

When this door is opened, a switch isolates the mains power and also enables the spindle lock to be engaged so that cutter blocks can be changed.

Conclusion

A beautifully made and robust machine from Italy; qualities that are reflected in the price.

It is quiet and easy to use, and the extra feature of a tilting arbor will be useful to most wood machinists. Although the spindle may not spend a lot of its time on the tilt, it will prove to be an invaluable feature when a project arrives that needs some trick mouldings.

There are a large number of useful accessories available from SCM for the T 40i , and the Italian machine will serve its owners well for many years. ∎

SECOND OPINION

Roger Smith

"I LIKE the robustness of the machine with its large, solid cast-iron bed, but I'm not too keen on the plastic handles and levers.

The tilting spindle opens up some new possibilities for mouldings, the four speeds are more than enough and the machine runs very quietly."

Guy Smith

"THE switchgear caused me some concern as it would be too easy to turn the machine on instead of releasing the brake.

Apart from this I think the T 40i is a well made, solid and powerful machine with good quality fences and accessories."

Rojek FS300 sp

Technical Editor **Alan Goodsell** finds this machine from the Czech Republic represents good value for money

SOLID CAST-IRON beds supported on a heavy sheet steel cabinet give an indication of the robustness of the FS300. As a testament to its strength, it stood up to, apparently, the driver unloading it by the radical expedient of opening the van doors and driving off like Damon Hill on the starting grid – allowing the machine to fly out of the back.

The FS300 was surprisingly unmangled after this, needing only a small amount of repair work before it was ready for this test. Few assembly clues were gleaned from the poorly translated and vaguely illustrated instruction manu-

BELOW: The Rojek FS300.

al. The parts manual doesn't run to English, but the exploded drawings are a help; with only a few parts to assemble, the machine goes together fairly logically.

Construction

The steel cabinet looks narrow for the size of the bed, and infeed and outfeed rollers are a must when machining long lengths of stock; to stop the machine from tipping it should be bolted down.

Three steel rings set into the solid cast-iron bed close up the spindle hole when machining short stock.

Delving into the machine, I found a further steel disc – presumably fitted to stop wood chippings finding their way into the depths of the spindle. However, it fouled the spindle shaft causing

sparks and some concern, so was quickly removed.

The hood is a large, solid casting and the fences, with solid beech (*Fagus sp*) cheeks, have nicely set-up micro-adjusters on both sides of the hood. The bolts that hold it to the bed have a fairly small diameter and could do with being more substantial to eliminate any possibility of snapping.

To comply with CE regulations a standard type of Shaw guard assembly is supplied. This works well enough but a certain amount of slack has to be allowed for when setting-up.

To make adjustments to the cutter block, the unit can be flipped-up to provide good access.

Setting-up

The rise-and-fall works smoothly, being well set for fine adjustments. Both the plastic operating wheel and the unusual but simple to use aluminium cam-lever for locking the spindle are conveniently placed on the side of the cabinet.

A window is set in the cabinet so that calibrations for the rise-and-fall can be seen; it is doubtful whether this could seriously be used for accurate setting-up, but as a guide it could be useful.

A large selection of collars on the spindle shaft allow a range of different thickness cutter blocks or tenoning discs to be used.

In the absence of a spindle-lock, a large Allen key has to be used in conjunction with a spanner to loosen or tighten the spindle nut. I would prefer to see a lock fitted as it is often difficult to wield both an Allen key and spanner at the same time, and

> "It is often difficult to wield both an Allen key and spanner at the same time, and knuckles will inevitably be skinned"

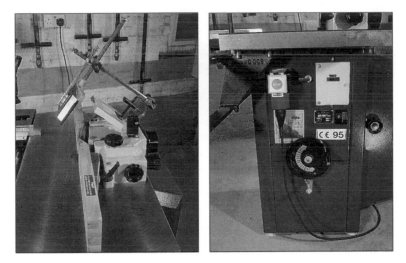

FAR LEFT: Good fence assembly with micro-adjusters to both sides.

LEFT: Switch can be padlocked for safety, rise-and-fall works well although height indicator, left of spec. plate, is only a rough guide when setting up.

knuckles will inevitably be skinned.

The Rojek spindle must be positioned at least 360mm, 14in away from the wall to allow the large, rear access door to be opened fully for speed changing. The three speeds available – 3,000, 6,000 and 9,000rpm – are more than sufficient for most jobs on this size of spindle.

Speeds can be changed fairly easily through the rear door, by slackening the motor and moving the belt to a different pulley. The only fiddly part of the process is to move, along with the belt, a 'C' bracket that is linked to a speed indicator on the outside of the machine.

This is best chucked away as it is difficult to shift, flimsy and precarious. This frequently seen device must be part of the CE regulations to ensure our safety, but will only be useful to some-one who can't remember more than three things at a time!

Motor, switchgear

The mains cable from the switch runs close to the rise-and-fall wheel, and I sometimes found it catching on my hand when rotating the wheel; if the machine were permanently installed the cable could be clipped to the cabinet out of harm's way.

A flap covering the switch has to be lifted to gain access to the on-switch; when the flap is let back down it becomes a large cut-off switch which can be padlocked to isolate the machine for safety.

The large 2.2kW, 3hp motor is quite noisy, but not too intrusive in a busy workshop with other machines and extractors running.

I had no problems running out some large mahogany (*Swietenia macrophylla*) mouldings.

Another safety feature is an electric brake that cuts in when

"To stop the machine from tipping it should be bolted down"

power is switched off; this brings the spindle to a rapid halt and once stopped there is a gentle hum for a few seconds which ceases when the spindle is released.

The block can then be swung by hand – isolating the mains power first, of course.

Sliding carriage

The sliding carriage, costing an extra £392 including VAT, complements the machine well. Built

to the same high standard, it has a cast-iron bed, a substantial chrome bar and a lower flat steel plate on which to run.

With a few bolts to hold large cast brackets for bar and steel plate, it is easy to fit. Once in place, it is a simple job to level the sliding table with the main bed by means of two adjusting bolts.

The carriage is a joy to use, and glides back and forward on its runners with a noticeable lack ➤

FACTS AND FIGURES

FS300 spindle moulder

Price:	£1150 including VAT
Overall dimensions:	1,026 x 952 x 606mm, 40³/₈ x 37¹/₂ x 24in
Size of table:	952 x 452mm, 37¹/₂ x18in
Height of table:	890mm, 35in
Spindle speeds:	3,000, 6,000, 9,000rpm
Spindle diameter:	30mm, 1¹/₈in
Motor:	2.2kW, 3hp
Weight:	140kg, 308lb

Sliding Carriage

Price:	£392 including VAT
Size of table:	390 x 500mm, 15³/₈ x 19³/₄in
Cut with fence extended:	1600mm, 63in
Weight:	52kg, 114lb

Contact: Jordan Wood Machinery (Tel: 0191 5840784)

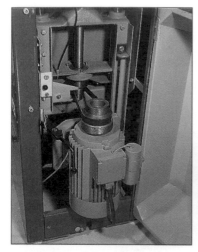

ABOVE: Rear door gives good access for speed changing, but the speed indicator bracket fails to please – see text.

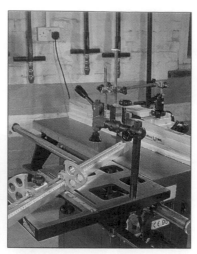

ABOVE: Well-made sliding carriage – this picture shows the fence in its second position, which looks a little insecure.

"When a company can produce a quality machine for the price of this one, a few cut corners can be forgiven"

NEW PLAYER

ROJEK IS A new name to most of us, but Jordan Woodmachinery Ltd have been importing this range of machines from the Czech Republic for about two years.

Chosen for solid build and highly competitive prices, Rojek machines look like becoming an established name in the woodworking world, not least because of

their use of cast-iron as standard – less common than it used to be.

The machines are available in either single or three-phase versions, and all carry a full **CE** accreditation and a one year guarantee.

Jordan also carry a wide range of rebuilt and used equipment; they can supply accessories, tooling and servicing.

BELOW: Alan Goodsell at the helm – this picture shows the sliding carriage's fence in a more sensible position, although it is not being used.

of unwanted slackness in travel.

A long aluminium fence can be fitted to either the front or back of the carriage to allow angles up to 45° either way to be machined; a calibration is set in as a guide for setting angles, but there are no stops for 0° or 45°.

With the fence positioned at the back of the bed, work is placed behind the fence away from the cut; this is not normal practice as this leaves only the hold down to resist the cutting force.

Flip-over stops

The substantial steel clamp looks like a dog bone, and can be set in one of two positions for differing widths of stock; a cam-clamp on top holds work securely.

The fence, with its wooden end to protect it and the cutter, can be extended to allow stock 1,760mm, 69$\frac{1}{4}$in long to be machined – but take care not to pull the extension piece too far, as it drops out of the end of the fence and is difficult to replace.

Three large, easy to set flip-over stops are provided; these are nicely firm, ensuring accuracy when machining. Make sure to allow for set-up pieces as the fence calibration, in common with that on most machines, is not to be relied on.

The sliding carriage is a solid extra providing valuable additional capabilities.

Conclusion

It was a pleasant surprise to use this machine after being accustomed to handling a large number of more commonly known brands. I found it to be a solid, no-nonsense piece of equipment; but like most machines on the market it has aspects that I would like to see improved.

However, when a company can produce a quality machine for the price of this one, a few cut corners can be forgiven. ■

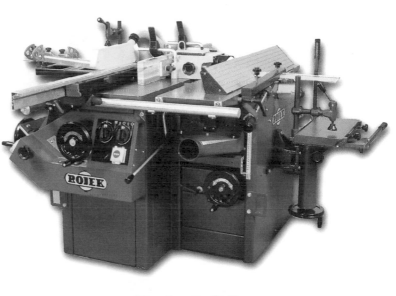
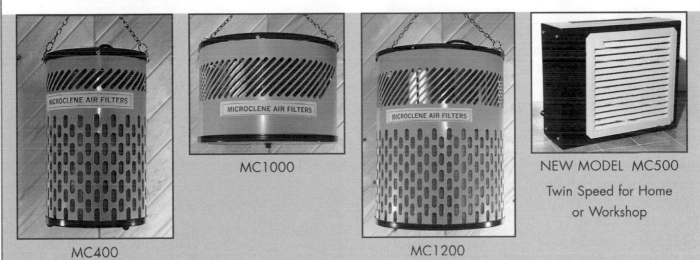

POOLEWOOD EURO 2000

- THE WORLD'S FIRST DIRECT-DRIVE LATHE

EURO 2000 WITH OPTIONAL BENCH & OUTBOARD TURNING REST

THE POOLEWOOD EURO 2000 IS PROBABLY THE MOST ADVANCED LATHE IN THE WORLD TODAY

Endorsed by seven of the world's top woodturners speaks for itself (how many lathes can boast this!!)

Direct Drive. There are pulleys or belts, and this cuts down the number of moving parts resulting in a quieter machine, it also does away with the power loss experienced through belt drives. None of this would have been possible without the

DAVE REEKS

development of the electronic motor computerised control panel complete with in-built micro processor which gives a speed range from zero to 3500 rpm without any noticeable power loss. The lathe has a cast iron bed, headstock, tailstock, x-slide, tool rest and even the motor has a cast iron housing.

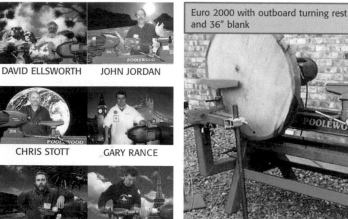

DAVID ELLSWORTH   JOHN JORDAN

CHRIS STOTT   GARY RANCE

ROLLY MUNRO   ALAIN MAILLAND

Euro 2000 with outboard turning rest and 36" blank

Dave Reeks & Jimmy Clewes proving two into one will go

Poolewood Machinery,
Pett Farm, Stockbury Valley, Sittingbourne, Kent,
ME9 7RJ
Tel: (44) 01622 884 651
Fax: (44) 01622 884 520
email: info@poolwood.ftech.co.uk

DON'T TAKE OUR WORD FOR IT, LISTEN TO WHAT THE EXPERTS SAY:

International Master-Turner David Ellsworth (U.S.A)

"The Euro 2000 is a superb lathe that far exceeded my expectations, I've used them all, and this machine has it all. I like it... A lot!"

International Hollow Form Artististic Woodturner John Jordan (U.S.A)

"Smooth, fast and powerful!"

International Bowl Master Chris Stott (U.K)

"I was able to turn 12" diameter logs at a much higher speed than normal, I can honestly say the Euro 2000 is the smoothest Lathe I have ever worked on."

International Master Gary Rance (U.K.)

"The Euro 2000 is quiet, smooth, powerful and a joy to use. Definitely the lathe for the 21st century."

International Woodturner Rolly Munro (New Zealand)

"The thing that impressed me was the smoothness, also the torque, it was unbelievable"

International Master of Hollow Forms Alain Mailland (France)

"The Euro 2000 performs like a Rolls Royce"

Dave Reeks (UK) Large Bowls, Platters & Hollow Forms

"I was asked to do a test report for the *Woodturning* magazine, and I was so impressed, I ordered one."

Sedgwick SM4 spindle moulder

Alan Goodsell puts this all-British machine to the test

S EDGWICK HAVE been manufacturing woodworking machinery for 50 years or so.

That the company survived a recession which saw the demise of other familiar British woodworking machine manufacturers is largely due to modernisation of their plant, this action increasing production efficiency and building up exports.

Although production has been streamlined, John Sedgwick and his co-directors have ensured that their company's legendary build quality hasn't been compromised; today's machines retain the robustness and solidity of the old school.

Construction

The Sedgwick SM4 is true to this tradition, and it is a joy to see a machine built to the strapping specifications of this one.

This no-frills machine has a sturdy cast-iron bed sitting on a heavy gauge steel cabinet. This strength combines with sturdy fences and strong control wheels and levers to ensure the machine is a sound long-term investment for continued commercial workshop use.

When removed, four massive, turned cast-iron bed rings leave a 255mm, 10in diameter hole — far beyond the capacity of any cutterblock that I have ever used.

The huge cavity below the bed has an outlet for air to escape, and provides good elbow room for setting up.

A skimpy manual gives brief but informative details about operating and wiring up. The exploded parts drawing shows how the SM4 is made, and will aid dismantling for maintenance purposes.

Because an insufficient number of spanners is supplied, a delve into the workshop toolkit for the necessary sizes will be required.

The professional presentation returns with the inclusion of mounting holes in the bed for a power feed — essential for producing a smooth finish and eliminating the fatigue of running long lengths of stock.

Setting-up

The rise-and-fall works smoothly, and fine gearing makes small adjustments to the height precise. The large operating wheel on the front is located in the right position for setting-up.

When setting the height of the cutter, crouching or kneeling down often provides a better line of sight onto the block. A large-locking lever is well placed directly above the wheel, gripping the shaft securely when tightened.

The 30mm, $1^3/_{16}$ in spindle has a large nut for fixing cutterblocks; unfortunately the spindle doesn't retract below the surface of the bed, so the Sedgewick can't be used as a flat surface on which to assemble projects. ➤

> "It is a joy to see a machine built to the strapping specifications of this one"

BELOW: A happy man — Alan Goodsell with the SM4

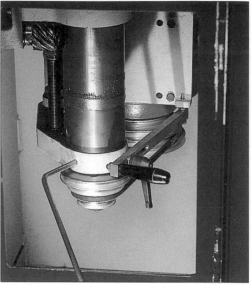

"The process is blissfully simple, without peculiar and awkward to set-up gimmicks"

The massive bed rings are impossible to lift out without first removing the spindle collars to create a gap large enough for fingers.

A large range of collars is supplied — this is a boon for those with a variety of cutterblocks and tenoning discs.

The spindle is locked without the benefit of a fussy built-in device; instead, a wonderfully simple length of bent steel bar is slid into the appropriate hole to lock the spindle securely. It is long enough to protrude through the access door to prevent it shutting, which in turn ensures the machine is isolated.

Hood and fences

The hood and fence is another substantial cast-iron assembly that could induce a hernia if lifted without assistance. It boasts a large, easily removed, casting on top that, when detached, gives good access to the cutterblock.

The well made Shaw guards are mounted on this plate, but some movement in this mounting remains after tightening up. This slack can be allowed for when setting-up, but finding it on a machine of this quality is a bit disappointing.

The Shaw guard fences are plywood and the face guard a huge 140mm, $5^{1}/_{2}$in wide. This gives the operator scope to use it full width, or to cut it down to suit the current job.

These days fences are frequently inferior, but Sedgwick have excelled with this design. They are made from 13mm, $^{1}/_{2}$in thick slabs of steel plate that won't warp or bend, providing a stable drilled backing on which users may easily attach cheeks of their choice.

Both the fences have well-made and precise micro-adjusters to set an offset for planing and some types of moulding.

The large and strong operating levers and handles on the assembly give confidence that enough force can be applied to ensure the fences stay in place.

Switchgear

Two basic and well-made switches are conveniently mounted around the right-hand side of the machine.

The rotating, padlockable isolating switch needs to be wired permanently into a mains power supply.

The on/off switch above has a push-on and a large locking-off switch which eliminates confusion.

In use

Pressing the on-button launches the large 3kW motor into life. It runs smoothly and is relatively quiet for an industrial-standard machine. The loose-top spindle — so-called because it can be replaced or changed easily, not because it wobbles about — is long, easily accommodating my 110mm, $4^{3}/_{8}$in wide cornice cutterblock.

I ran a cornice moulding for a kitchen project on 160mm, $6^{1}/_{4}$in wide stock that didn't slow the powerful motor at all.

Hitting the off-button brings the motor to a rapid halt. With the motor stopped, however, the spindle is stiff to turn by hand for setting-up purposes even after the mains power has been isolated.

Speeds

Opening the large door on the right of the machine gives good access for changing any of the four speeds. Once open a switch ensures the machine is isolated.

Slacken the motor with its ratchet lever, swinging it forward to loosen the belt; move the belt to the desired pulley and reverse the process to tension the belt. The process is blissfully simple, without peculiar and awkward to set-up gimmicks.

Sliding carriage

Made, like the spindle moulder, from great lumps of cast-iron, the

"A strapping piece of C-section steel is bolted to the bed at 90° – this is the fence"

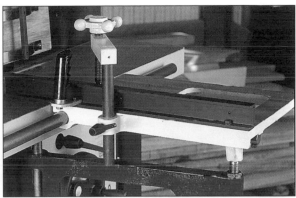

ABOVE: Sliding carriage with substantial hold-down

RIGHT: Why can't all switchgear be this straightforward?

LEFT: Fence doesn't let the machine down

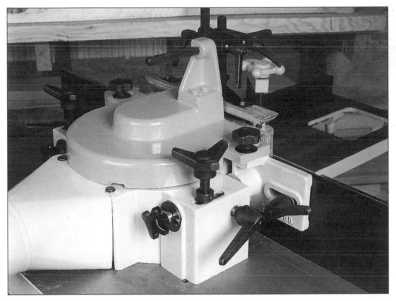

sliding carriage is an optional extra costing £481 including VAT.

Fitting it to the main machine is a bit fiddly as the only adjustment to the height is dependent on two bolts in slots in the spindle's bed.

The swinging arm has a pin that fits sloppily into a sliding collar under the carriage's bed. As the role of this pin is to support the end of the bed — which it does — the slack isn't important.

The sliding action felt gritty, but some grease and use would probably overcome this in time.

The surface milling on the bed isn't very smooth, and there are shallow steps about 60mm, $2^3/_8$in apart, from each pass through the milling machine. They could affect accuracy if a piece of stock being machined happened to be a width where the step would cause it to rock slightly.

A strapping piece of C-section steel is bolted to the bed at 90° — this is the fence.

Cross-fences are most commonly used at right angles, and this one provides a rigid, fixed fence for the task. Alternatively it can be used as a starting point to create a fence of any angle.

A hefty hold-down clamp, as

seen on the company's mortiser, is large enough to fix a piece of wood securely to the bed ready for machining. Take care not to drop the main bar down too far, as it will foul the sliding carriage swinging arm and leave you wondering why your piece of wood won't reach the cutter.

Conclusion

This professional machine can easily be tailored for the purchaser's own purposes. The SM4 is sturdy enough to withstand the rigours of a hard life in the workshop.

Praise is also due for the fences; built to a standard for which every machine manufacturer should aim, they are solid and easy to set precisely.

There are no superfluous features, like height calibrations or external speed indicators, usually either virtually useless or a pain in the neck to set up.

Although purchasers of these machines should have the nous to rectify the minor niggles I have identified, Sedgwick could address them at little cost.

However, I have no hesitation in recommending this machine to anyone, as I am a traditionalist where woodworking machines are concerned — and proud of it!

FACTS AND FIGURES

SM4 Spindle Moulder

Price	
Three phase	£2,226 inc VAT
Single phase	£2,344 inc VAT
Overall Dimensions	1,200 x 1,000 x 650mm, $47^1/_4$ x $39^3/_8$ x $25^5/_8$in
Size of table	1,000 x 650mm, $39^3/_8$ x $25^5/_8$8in
Height of table	880mm, $34^5/_8$in
Spindle speeds	3,000, 4,500, 6,000, 8,000rpm
Spindle diameter	30mm
Motor	3kW
Weight	430kg, 947lb

Sliding Carriage

Price	£481 incl VAT
Size of table	450 x 300mm, $17^3/_4$ x $11^3/_4$in
Weight	50kg, 110lb

Combined price

SM4 + sliding carriage, three phase	£2,632 inc VAT
SM4 + sliding carriage, single phase	£2,749 VAT

A smaller SM3 spindle moulder is available at prices starting from £1,756 including VAT.

● *Availability:* Contact M. Sedgwick & Co Ltd, Swinnow Lane, Leeds LS13 4QG, tel 0113 2570637, fax 0113 2393412.

LAB 30 combina

Technical editor **Alan Goodsell** tests a midrange universal machine

PHOTOGRAPHY BY
ANTHONY BAILEY

BELOW: The Lab 30 universal in the testing hands of F&C's Technical Editor — as can be seen from the background, there's a lot at stake.

THE LAB 30 ARRIVES as a compact, shrink-wrapped unit weighing 470kg, 1036lb. Fences and guards are boxed ready to put onto the machine; all the tools required for assembly are provided in a tool bag. Then the fun begins...

...I looked to the poorly translated multi-lingual manual for instructions – and spent the best part of a day putting the machine together with the aid of well-drawn diagrams in the parts list.

Buyers would be well advised to allow at least a day to assemble and familiarise themselves with this machine.

Construction

The machine is well constructed, and has cast iron beds sitting on a heavy sheet metal stand. The main switch panel and saw extractor outlet are contained within a good quality fibreglass housing.

Three separate single phase 3hp motors power the planer/thicknesser, spindle and saw. This motor rating necessitates permanent wiring into a 15Amp power supply.

A three phase version of the LAB 30 is available at the same price as the single phase machine.

Planer/thicknesser

The first job is to set the three planer knives in the good quality cutter block by flipping the planer beds up and placing an aluminium setting tool on the block.

Slacken the locking bolts and the knives spring up to meet the setting tool; then the locking bolts can be tightened.

Once all three of the knives have been set the beds can be flipped down and the out-feed bed lined up, with a straight edge, to the planer knives.

This is a quick and common method of setting planer knives. More accurate, but time-consuming, is to align the knives to a straight edge put on the out-feed bed. This ensures the full length of all the knives is perfectly lined up.

Planer fence

The slightly fiddly job of fitting the extremely well made and designed flip-up planer guard is followed by

tion

the task of putting on the extruded aluminium planer fence.

This fence lets the machine down. It is awkward to use, and an add-on support to prevent the fence from flexing is unsatisfactory.

The longer of the two extrusions is used for the planer fence. This is mounted on a cast iron plate that is also employed for the sawbench fence.

The triangular fence can be fitted on any of its three faces, but would normally be used long point down to enable angles from vertical to 45° to be achieved.

A planer guard in this orientation covers the exposed blade.

Easily adjustable

The long planer beds are easily adjusted by unlocking a metal lever and turning a cylindrical aluminium handle. I checked the beds for flatness and found them to be true.

Removable finger sections in the throat cut down on noise and aid waste removal.

Lift the beds up for thicknessing, ensuring that the out-feed bed is raised first. Flip the neat extractor hood into place and lock it by means of a sprung steel catch.

The hood sits at an upright angle so that the extractor pipe doesn't foul timber being fed through the thicknesser.

The thicknessing bed has a smooth-working single pillar rise and fall, and has no unwanted slack at either the top or bottom of its range.

Accessible wheel

Rise and fall is by means of a good quality easily accessible wheel; the adjacent locking lever is also easily reached.

Calibrations on the rise and fall scale should be used only as a rough guide; fine adjustments are easily made, though, with a nicely geared rate of movement.

The drive feed lever is well placed and has a strong spring to ensure it stays in place. The feed should be disengaged when overhand-planing to minimise wear on the drive-wheel tyre.   ➤

ABOVE: Overhand planing using the long fence.

ABOVE: Thicknessing is efficient... but not a one-man job.

"It would be an interesting sight to see one person launching themselves around the flipped-up beds to catch short stock passing through the thicknesser"

ABOVE: Ripping is trouble free; scoring-saw accessory is a bargain.

ABOVE: Sliding carriage and fence get the seal of approval.

The machine runs quietly and the motor barely slowed when some 150mm, 6in wide boards of oak (*Quercus robur*) with a 2.5mm, $^3/_{32}$in cut were fed through the thicknesser.

The substantial anti-kickback dogs inspire confidence and the spiral cut in-feed roller and rubber coated out-feed roller leave no marks on fine cuts.

The LAB 30's manual claims it to be a one-man machine. It would make an interesting sight to see one person launching themselves around the flipped up beds to catch short stock passing through the thicknesser.

Sawbench
The shorter of the two extruded aluminium fences is fitted on an easily removed mounting bracket – which is also used for the planer.

The fence assembly is designed to do everything – and does – but it is awkward to operate and difficult to set accurately even though it has a crude micro adjuster.

However, a neat, adjustable pointer on the mounting bracket means the calibrations on the fence slide bar can be relied on.

Making a test cut and setting the pointer to this measurement calibrates the scale so that all measurements will be correct until the sawblade is changed.

An aluminium plate covers the hole in the cast iron bed through which the blade and guard disappear when not in use.

The rise and fall and the tilt arbor of the saw operate very smoothly and

are well geared for fine adjustment. The tilt has adjustable stops for vertical and 45°; its locking knob is within easy reach.

Blade capacity
The LAB 30 is supplied with a 250mm, 10in diameter TCT sawblade with a riving knife and guard to suit. It has the capacity for a 300mm, 12in diameter blade, but that would entail replacing the riving knife and fence.

Axminster accidentally supplied me with a 200mm, 8in diameter blade which was employed for the photographs, but I used my own 250mm, 10in diameter TCT blade for the test.

The saw runs smoothly and quietly and coped well when some large section mahogany (*Swietenia macrophylla*) was run through it.

Saw scribe
The availability of a scribing saw attachment – an optional extra priced at £139 including VAT – is a major advantage of this machine's sawbench.

This adds a small diameter sawblade, positioned in front of the main blade, set to cut a shallow groove in the underside of the stock prior to the cut of the main blade.

This eliminates breakout from the downcut of the main blade and is essential for a good finish when cutting melamine-faced or veneered sheet material, or when cross-cutting solid wood.

> "A bonus of the tidy design is a lack of bits sticking out to snag one's delicate body parts"

Sliding carriage
The sliding carriage is very neat and well made although not large enough to cope with 2440 x 1220mm, 8 x 4ft sheet material comfortably.

An aluminium bed slides easily on two solid steel bars. A pressed steel bed extension can be attached either to the sliding carriage bed or to the left of the LAB 30's main cast iron bed.

Stops can be set so that the carriage doesn't run off either end of the bars, and a bolt engages to lock the carriage in the central position.

The fence for the sliding carriage is an aluminium extrusion and can be set to angles either by using the preset indents, or by locking at any position in between.

It is rather jerky to move, but once locked it remains firm. Tilting the saw arbor enables compound mitres to be cut.

Telescopic extension
A useful telescopic extension to the fence provides capacity for sawing widths up to 1980mm, 78in.

The spring-loaded and easy to set up stops on the fence employ one of the best designs I have seen for a long time, allowing two different lengths to be set at once – a real time-saver when embarking on a production run.

A substantial cam-action hold-down clamp is fitted to the sliding carriage. Large levers provide enough power to clamp wood firmly to the bed.

Because the clamp is a fixed length it has to be swung to the left for narrow stock, so putting the clamping action quite a distance from the saw or spindle.

BELOW: Spindle moulder is a good performer.

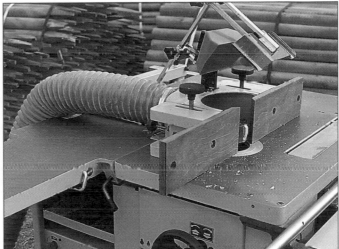
BELOW: Neat flip-up Shaw guard assembly.

Switches

The main switch panel is housed in a fibreglass moulding on the end of the machine. A rotating function selector switch, a large self-locking off-switch, the only on-switch on the machine and the spindle speed indicator are included.

To stop unauthorised use an isolator switch with a padlock hasp cover is situated to the left of the main panel. When the cover is flipped shut it automatically switches mains power off.

There are two other large self-locking off-switches: one in the position for spindle moulding; one in the position for overplaning.

Spindle moulder

The spindle is as easy to set up as any I have used. Three removable aluminium rings in the bed support small stock. They are a little stiff to remove but will loosen up with use.

A large door on the end of the machine gives good access for changing any of the four speeds. Opening the door cuts off the mains power and also enables the knob-operated spindle lock to engage.

The v-belt is placed on the selected pulley after the belt tension is released with a plastic ratchet lever on the motor bracket.

A strange, metal-plate finger device connected by bowden cable to a spindle speed indicator on the main switch panel has to be centred ➤

ABOVE: Well designed ring-fences are welcome.

SPECIFICATIONS

PLANER:
Motor – 3hp, 2,235W
Surfacing table overall size – 1480 x 300mm, 58¼ x 11¾in
Thicknessing table size – 540 x 300mm, 21¼ x 11¾in
Maximum thickness capacity – 230mm, 9in
Feed speed – 7m per minute, 275in per minute
Rpm – 5200
Knives – 3

SAW:
Motor – 3hp, 2,235W
Rpm – 4000
Maximum depth of cut at 90° – 70mm, 2¾in
Maximum depth of cut at 45° – 63mm, 2½in
Saw diameter – 250mm, 10in

SPINDLE:
Motor – 3hp, 2,235W
Rpm – 1,400, 3,500, 6,000, 8,000
Spindle diameter – 30mm
Spindle capacity – 136mm, 5³⁄₈in

MORTISER:
Rpm – 4500
Table size – 200 x 425mm, 8 x 16¾in
Stroke. traverse x longitudinal x vertical – 160 x 135 x 100mm, 6¼ x 5¼ x 4in
Chuck capacity – 0 - 16mm, 0 - ⅝in

PRICE:
A.P.T.C. LAB 30 costs £3,399 including VAT

Contact:
Axminster
Power Tool
Centre
(Tel: 01297 33656)

ALFRESCO VIEW

A glitch in best laid plans resulted in F&C being grateful for the use of an unphotogenic but workmanlike barn at Silvester Engineering, Billingshurst, West Sussex in which to test and photograph this machine. Thanks to Pete and Richard.

be possible to swing the block by hand for setting up and checking if the cutters foul.

The sliding carriage intrudes slightly on access to the spindle moulder, but if a long run is anticipated it can easily be removed.

Slot mortiser

A slot mortiser isn't supplied as standard, but one can be obtained as an extra for £493.50 including VAT.

Conclusion

This machine suffers from drawbacks common to other combinations.

The first is the combined sawbench and planer fence system. It does all it is supposed to do, but it is awkward to use and has too much flexibility – the wrong kind! – to inspire confidence.

The second is the lack of on-switches; one on the end of the machine is just not enough. I have an aversion to walking around a running woodworking machine, and like to be in full control of all the switching functions from the operating position.

Apart from these two gripes I liked the LAB 30. It is well designed and solidly constructed, and has good capacity for its size.

A bonus of the tidy design is a lack of bits sticking out on which to snag one's delicate body parts.

The three powerful motors run very quietly, and dust extraction is well thought out. The flip-over hood is a particularly neat design.

A set of extra wheels to aid the machine's manoeuvrability costs £148 inc VAT, making the LAB 30 viable for an amateur or professional with a smaller workshop. ■

on the belt; although it's handy to see the speed selected the device is a pain to alter.

Once the door is shut the rise and fall wheel can be replaced. Two good quality plastic wheels are supplied for use with any of the operating shafts onto which they slide.

The rise and fall is very smooth and well geared for fine adjustments. The locking knob is small, with a flimsy bolt that may not stand up to continual workshop abuse.

Fence and guards

The good quality cast aluminium hood has plywood cheeks that are easily positioned to close the throat on the cutter.

The micro-adjuster on the out-feed fence is a useful feature for planing or for when a moulding needs a step in the fence for support.

Initially stiff to operate, it will loosen up with use – but the knob could do with being larger.

A well designed flip-up Shaw guard is supplied; it has some play but, with experience, this can be allowed for when setting up.

Welcome accessories are a pair of well designed 100mm, 4in and

150mm, 6in ring fences which attach to a bonnet hood with an extractor outlet.

Cutter blocks are secured to the spindle with a collar incorporating a large captive Allen head bolt. A useful variety of different width collars is supplied, allowing a range of block widths to be used.

The quiet but powerful spindle motor coped well with the mouldings I ran through it. The self-braking motor is good for safety, but if the brake could be released – having isolated the machine first – it would

"It's a very quiet machine which runs without vibration and has plenty of power in all functions"

OTHER TESTERS REPORT

PAUL RICHARDSON
"At first sight the LAB 30 appears to be robustly made and tidily designed. The main planer sawbench fence is a bit of a dog's dinner but seems to work.

The sliding carriage works smoothly and I was impressed by the adjustable stops. It's a very quiet machine which runs without vibration and has plenty of power in all funtions.

The optional scoring attachment for the sawbench is an unusual feature on a combination machine. If I owned one of these machines I would certainly fit one."

PETE SILVESTER
"I immediately liked the machine as it is obviously good quality. I found it easy to change from one operation to another and the motors are noticeably quiet and smooth.

The planer works very well apart from the fence which I found troublesome.

The spindle moulder is difficult to switch on as the switch is quite a reach over the machine, but if Axminster decide not to collect the machine I can assure them I will give it a good home!"

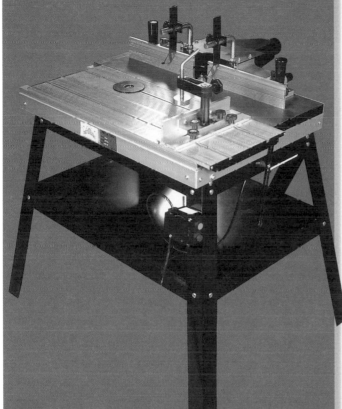

Robland LX310

With some help from his friends, our Technical Editor **Alan Goodsell** put Robland's classic machine through its many and varied paces

PHOTOGRAPHY BY
ANTHONY BAILEY

BELOW: The Robland LX310 in all its glory.

TO TEST THE Robland LX310 combination machine I drafted in some help from three friends and fellow cabinetmakers based in West Sussex. Roger Smith, Guy Smith (no relation), Mark Constanduros and I tested the combination machine from Wilson Brothers Ltd for a few days — to give it a thorough checkout.

Our first impression was unanimous — it's huge! It measures approximately 2100 by 2400mm, 7 by 8ft, including the sliding carriage, and weighs 400kg, 881lbs. We shoehorned it into Roger's workshop, which already boasts a full complement of individual woodworking machines. Then we had to make working space around it! There is a wheel kit available,

normally costing £211 plus VAT, currently offered free with the machine. A turntable costing £305 plus VAT is also available. Either of these extras would make life easier in restricted space.

Construction

The LX310 is not only large, it is solidly built, having a thick gauge sheet steel casing which supports substantial cast iron beds. The LX310 includes the basic functions of a combination machine, having a planer thicknesser, spindle moulder, bench saw and slot mortiser.

Each of the three main functions has its own single phase 3hp motor. The slot mortiser runs on the end of the planer shaft. A three phase version of the machine is also available.

Sawbench

A real pleasure after using some other combination machines is that there is no belt changing involved between different functions. Just turn the selector switch to the desired setting, in this case the saw, and you're ready for action.

Operated by a large turn-to-lock lever, the rise and fall on the saw blade is very smooth. The high

combination

gearing means that a short movement of the lever will raise or lower the blade quite a lot, making it a little difficult for fine adjustment when sawing a rebate or groove. A crudely made crank operates the tilting arbor, and a helpful touch is that there is no need to remove the table insert to allow the blade to tilt. There is no positive stop for 90°.

When I started to set up I was disappointed to find that the rip fence allows a maximum cutting width of only 242mm, 9^1/$_2$in. The fence slide is short because the planer bed extends beyond the front of the sawbench. I then found that you could use the planer fence — which I will comment on later   on the other side of the machine to achieve a useful 600mm, 24in width of cut.

Switch panel

Switching for all of the functions is carried out at a main panel, on which there is an on/off-switch with a rotating function-selecting switch alongside. A padlockable isolating switch is to the left of the main panel. Two other off-switches are conveniently placed, but I feel it would be safer if there were also on-switches at these positions. This would eliminate the temptation to reach over a running machine rather than take the safer but annoying alternative of walking around.

An impressive feature of this machine is its quiet operation in all functions. Once the saw is switched on the singing of the supplied TCT blade is almost louder than the quiet motor.

I ran some 50mm, 2in English oak through the saw and it coped with it well, leaving an almost planed finish. After this I ripped up a large batch of 25mm, 1in thick beech and found that the saw cut straight and true, with plenty of power, only slowing when there was a severe pinch before the kerf reached the

riving knife, due to the cut releasing extreme tension in some of the pieces of beech. This would happen on most saws.

When the main dust extraction point was connected to a reasonable extractor there was virtually no airborne dust, and there is also a point on the crown guard on which a small extraction pipe can be connected.

Sliding carriage

The large, cast sliding carriage runs smoothly on two adjustable solid steel bars, with further support from an odd steel bar leg. A telescopic arm provides support for the end of the carriage. This is rigid when close

"Once the saw is switched on the singing of the TCT blade is almost louder than the motor"

in, with only a small amount of vertical movement when extended. The fence is made of extruded aluminium with a primitive locking system for setting the fence angle. The roller fitted to the end of the table is useful when cutting sheet material, as is a steel flip-over stop, although this is a little stiff to operate. A nice cam-lock clamp is supplied but the small plastic wing nuts are too tiny to tighten up well. ➤

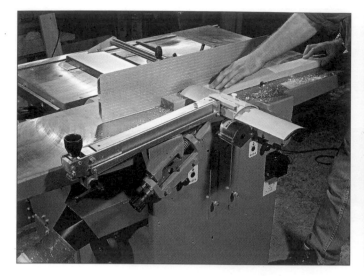

The fence system looks like a bit of an afterthought, but, as much as I disliked it for its flimsy feel, I found that it worked well and accurately.

Planer thicknesser

Setting up the planer thicknesser for overhand planing is conventional, with both of the long cast infeed and outfeed beds adjustable. I did check the beds for flatness and found them to be very slightly hollow, but not enough to worry about.

The plastic knobs for bed adjustment annoyed me but they do the job. I just don't like plastic.

I now get to the worst part of the machine — the planer fence. This is an aluminium extrusion with a steel slide bar and a cast mounting plate.

The way it is designed makes it impossible to lock the tilt solidly, and it moves when wide stock is edged. The ratchet levers tend to foul each other when the fence is set for wide planing. I would throw it away and have a proper one made.

> "The well designed extractor hood flips over the exposed cutter block"

The planer guard, however, is pleasingly designed and works extremely well. A turn of the plastic knob raises or lowers it and a small nylon knob locks the guard in the set in or out position.

Reach around to the switch panel and select the planer symbol on the selector switch, then switch on. An additional off-switch is located right by the infeed table but again, there is no on-switch. The 3hp motor runs quietly at 4500rpm and the three knife block left a fine finish on some 200mm, 10in wide pieces of oak which I put over it.

Apart from the fence I liked the solid construction and long beds. While overhand planing the mortiser could snag the operator's legs if left in place, it is designed to be easily removed.

For thickness planing, the surfacing beds are flipped into an upright position. First, each bed's metal lever is turned one quarter of a turn to release; the beds are then lifted up and locked into position.

The infeed side of the LX310 is fitted with a mounting plate for the spindle power-feed which restricts access to the lever. Watch out for the sharp edge under the power-feed casting — it's keen enough to sharpen your pencil or finger on!

Extractor hood

The well-designed extractor hood then flips over the exposed cutter block ready to be plugged into the dust extractor. A good tip is to fit a right angle pipe to the hood to stop the timber feeding through the thicknesser from snagging the ribbed extractor pipe. The central column for the rise and fall moves smoothly and remains rigid at the top and bottom of its movement. A plastic wheel operates the long-legged rise and fall gearing and again fine adjustment is difficult. This is one of the worst places from which to reach the on-switch — although there is an off-switch nearby. When the machine is running, the all-steel infeed and outfeed rollers are engaged by flipping up the control lever. I fed some 200mm, 10in wide oak through the anti kick-back dogs and set a cut of about 2.5mm, $^3/_{32}$in. The machine took it in, barely complained, and passed it out the other end with a smooth finish.

A drawback with thicknessing is that two people will be needed, one to feed the timber in and one to take it out. If you were to try to use it on your own, a pair of running shoes would make getting around the flipped-up beds easier.

Mortiser

The mortiser is an optional extra costing £395 plus VAT.

With the planer beds level, fit the planer guard then place the mortiser by fitting it onto the two mounting bolts.

Running on the end of the planer shaft there is an enclosed chuck with a capacity of 0-16mm, 0-$^5/_8$in which takes the slot mortising cutters. To find the locking bolt for this, through a gap in the housing, you have to put your fingers at risk by spinning the planer block.

The unit is solidly made, with the bed sliding two ways — one way for depth of cut and the other for width of mortise. It is operated by two levers and the bed moves smoothly both ways. Stops are fitted to set up

the dimension of mortise, and there is a rise and fall mechanism for positioning the mortise.

The work is secured to the bed with the clamp from the sliding carriage, and a back-stop can also be set to ensure it doesn't move when plunging the cut.

From this operating position switching on is a nightmare as the on-switch is too far away. This means walking around the machine. I found this really frustrating as the mortiser tends to be switched on and off frequently.

Juddering

I find that these types of mortiser tend to judder when large cuts are taken. I used a 12mm, $^1/2$in cutter in oak and certainly this resulted in some vibration. This is due to the long cutters required to get a useable depth of mortise. I have mixed feelings about this mortiser as I am used to — and prefer — chisel mortisers which allow good visibility and fast working. With a slot mortiser of this type work seems to proceed slowly, but, due to its build quality, this example seems better than some.

Spindle moulder

Moving the sliding carriage to the right gives clear access to the spindle moulder. The telescopic arm of the carriage appears to be in just the right position to trip up the operator, but if the end of the carriage is lifted slightly the threaded support bar drops out and allows the arm to be swung in tight to the machine, out of harm's way. The saw with its guard is then wound down below the bed table and the aluminium insert replaced. Once set up in this way there is a large uninterrupted bed. For moulding short stock three

removable bed inserts are supplied.

Under the bed is found a wheel with a locking lever to effect the precise and smooth rise and fall. Also under the bed is the lever for locking the spindle shaft when changing the cutter block.

Spindle guard

The spindle guard and fence assembly consists of a large iron casting with an aluminium fence. The two parts of the split fence are adjusted by means of small wing nuts which close the gap to the minimum required for the cutter block. The left-hand fence can also be adjusted in a similar way to the infeed table on a planer, although the step is on the outfeed. This is to allow for the cut on some types of moulding.

The shaw guard supplied can be adjusted to take stock sizes to about 178 x 200mm, 7 x 8in. It is a little springy but, with a bit of practice, this springiness can be used as part of the setting up procedure. A quick release lever enables the guard to be swung out of the way to give access for setting up.

Spindle moulding is the only function on the machine which gives full access to the switchgear — not a bad thing.

The spindle has a brake which engages very quickly when the machine is switched off.

The drawback of this is that the brake stays engaged even when the machine is idle, which makes setting up difficult — but not as difficult as losing a finger. One of the standard 'pre-flight' checks after setting up is to test for free movement of the cutter block by hand-rotating it; this is not possible with the brake engaged. Once switched on the quietness is noticeable, and when I

ran some mouldings in oak the machine didn't slow down at all.

The sliding carriage can be used for tenoning or scribing. I found the clamp too far from the cutter block, so that short rails would be impossible to machine on their ends without additional clamping.

A range of extra fences and guards is available.

Conclusion

Combination machines have a great deal to live up to. They have to compete with stand-alone machines which can be left set up; if you have forgotten to machine a component, you can go back again. A combination machine requires a very disciplined approach, making sure that all the components plus spares and setting up pieces are complete before moving on to the next stage. However, I feel this is a principle which should be adhered to in any workshop, whatever type of machines are used.

Space is something that most people have to consider and an advantage of a combination machine is in having most of the basic woodworking functions in one machine. But bear in mind that a large amount of working space will be required around it.

Quibbles

I feel the LX310 is let down slightly by its peripheral parts. The fences are of poor quality but work well, with the exception of the planer fence which doesn't. I also wonder how long they will last.

Switchgear is the other major bugbear. I have to ask how difficult it would be to fit on-switches with the off-switches, so eliminating the danger of reaching over a running

ABOVE LEFT: Spindle moulding with the sliding carriage; note hold-down position.

ABOVE: Using the slot mortiser.

"A pair of running shoes would make getting around the flipped-up beds easier"

➤

BELOW RIGHT: Quality of the castings helps performance.

machine or the inconvenience of spending all day walking around it.

Solid, reliable, quiet

Apart from those few faults I did like this machine as it is well designed and solid. It feels reliable and has a notable lack of vibration, and for a woodworking machine it is very quiet when running. It would suit someone with a small business, it would serve as a backup machine for a larger business, or it would be good for an experienced amateur with a large workshop.

We tested Robland's top of the range combination machine. The range from this reputable, long established company also includes the X310, with the standard smaller sliding table, and the X260 which has a narrower planer bed. ■

Our intrepid team: from the left Mark Constanduros, Guy Smith, Roger Smith and F&C's Technical Editor Alan Goodsell.

OTHER TESTERS REPORT

ROGER SMITH

"I've always had individual machines so it was of great interest to have this combination in my workshop. I found it to be solidly made with the exception of the fences, in particular the planer fence. I liked the thicknesser as it left no step on the end of the wood — a common problem with thicknessers. The spindle felt a little inaccessible because of the sliding carriage, but I liked the micro adjustment on the spindle fence. I wouldn't swap my individual machines for it — but then I wouldn't swap them for any combination machine."

GUY SMITH

"I liked this machine. It's solid and although I didn't like the quality of the fences and knobs, they functioned accurately. The saw bench has every feature you will need and the sliding carriage coped well unless very large sheet material was used. I would save the money on the slot mortiser and put it towards a stand-alone chisel mortiser. The machine seemed to have plenty of power and is very quiet. The thicknesser has a good depth of cut and I liked the neat flip-over hood. Extraction is well sorted on each function."

MARK CONSTANDUROS

"The machine seemed very large but well made. I found my way round it quickly with all functions logical to set up. I wasn't fond of the slot mortiser as I am too used to our ancient chisel mortiser, but it does the job. The switchgear is good and I like the three sensitive, locking off-switches — but I would like to see more convenient on-switches. The fences on the machine worked well but the quality could be improved. All the moving parts were smooth to operate and the machine has all the power I would need."

TECHNICAL DATA FOR ROBLAND LX310

Price as tested - £3,934 plus VAT.

PLANER ....
Motor – 3hp, 2,235W
Table sizes – 310 x 1440mm, 12³/₁₆ x 56 1¹/₁₆in
Maximum thicknessing capacity – 230mm, 9in
Feed speed – 6m, 20ft per minute
Rpm – 4500
Knives – 3

SAW ....
Motor – 3hp, 2,235W
Rpm – 4000
Maximum depth of cut at 90° – 85mm, 3³/₈in
Maximum depth of cut at 45° – 55mm, 2¹/₈in
Saw table size – 800 x 445mm, 31¹/₂ x 17¹/₄in
Saw diameter – 250mm, 10in
Arbor diameter – 30mm
Maximum length of crosscut – 1290mm, 50³/₄in
Maximum width of crosscut – 610mm, 24in

SPINDLE MOULDER ....
Motor – 3hp, 2,235W
Rpm – 6000
Spindle diameter – 30mm
Spindle capacity – 125mm, 5in
Rise and fall – 140mm, 5¹/₂in

MORTISER..
Rpm – 4500
Table size – 200 x 425mm, 8 x 16³/₄in
Stroke (in x out x up) – 165 x 140 x 85mm,
6¹/₂x 5¹/₂ x 3¹/₈in.
Chuck capacity – 0-16mm, 0-⁵/₈in.

CONTACT: Wilson Brothers Ltd, Head Office, Springhead Enterprise Park, Springhead Road, Northfleet, Kent DA11 8HL
Tel: 01474 561414
Fax: 01474 561515

Holzher

Router

(HOLZ HER) ## 2356 Advanced Electronic Router

"Handles Beautifully"

Ron Fox Traditional Woodworking

VRT Full-Wave Electronics with Gentle Start, Variable Speed & Over-Load Protection.

Fine Adjustment of the Routing Depth using the Setting Wheel.

Locking Lever for Rapid Adjustment of the Routing Depth.

Rip Fence with Fine Adjustment & Scale Division of 0.1mm.

Spindle Locking Device.

Power input 1010 W. Power output 530 W.

8mm Chuck supplied with 1/4 Collet.

Routing Depth 50mm. Depth Adjustment 0-50mm.

Depth Stop 3 position. Speed 8000-25000/ min.

Cable 4m. Weight 2.7Kg.

GERMAN
2 YEAR
GUARANTEE
· 1914 ·
· 1914 ·
ENGINEERING

A strange combination

Rounding off a series of combination machine tests, Technical Editor **Alan Goodsell** puts the Kity K310 Ti through its paces with help from **Anthony Bailey**

STRICTLY SPEAKING the Kity isn't a full-blown combination machine, as the 609 spindle moulder-sawbench is one unit and the 638 planer-thicknesser is another.

The two machines can, however, be bolted together in one huge unit – if the purchaser has the nerve to drill holes in his spanking new acquisition – or used as separates.

Assembly is a fairly logical process, which is just as well as the manuals are brief and poorly translated.

The construction of these machines differs from those tested in previous issues as they have cast aluminium beds; although this means no rusting, I do wonder if they will stand the test of time during hard workshop use.

Sturdy fabricated steel cabinets support the beds, and the machines are bristling with switches.

Separate motors

With the exception of the 2653 slot mortiser which runs off the end of the planer shaft, separate motors drive each function.

Furnituremaker Anthony Bailey evaluated the planer-thicknesser and slot mortiser while I checked out the spindle moulder-sawbench with sliding carriage.

Sawbench

The good quality 250mm, 10in TCT blade on the sawbench has a rather mean plastic crown guard, but does the job and is quick to remove and replace. A large but flimsy plate in the bed is removed to provide good access to the arbor for blade changing.

The calibration on the rise-and-fall adjustment is useful as a rough guide, while the angle calibration for the tilting arbor proved to be quite accurate.

All operate smoothly and are ➤

PHOTOGRAPHY BY
ANTHONY BAILEY

**BELOW LEFT:
Kity 310 Ti
combination...**

**BELOW: ...or not.
Semi-separate
design adds
versatility.**

ABOVE: Ripping on the 609.

ABOVE RIGHT: Crosscutting – before the fuse blew...

ABOVE FAR RIGHT: Spindle-moulder function works well.

well geared for fine adjustments.

Sealed switchgear is well placed just to the left of the operating position for sawing, and the lockable isolator and selector switches are lower and to the right.

Rip fence

The rip fence is a good effort but the cast aluminium mounting bracket isn't well finished and the micro-adjuster is vague – I've never really understood why micro-adjusters are fitted to saw fences as no-one ever seems to use them (*speak for yourself – Editor*).

The fence can be orientated in two ways for ripping either thick or thin stock. Watch out for the sharp end on the extrusion as it is liable to cut fingers when being adjusted back and forwards; the fit on the mounting bracket is too tight.

The versatile mitre fence is well made and can be used in slots on either side of the blade.

A long sawing session was aborted after a fuse in the main switch blew. Because each of the three fuses fitted to the Kity differ they cannot be swapped around.

Before this happened it had coped well with some 25mm, 1in softwood and when linked to the workshop extractor the neat internal ducting took the dust away effectively.

The spindle extractor outlet is to the side of the outlet for the sawbench, so a swap from one to the other is easily accomplished.

Spindle moulder

The spindle arbor tilts – not a common feature on expensive stand-alone machines let alone on a combination.

Aluminium beds for both the sawbench and spindle are utilised from other separate machines in the Kity range, and are steel–dowelled together to provide a level surface when joined.

Good quality plastic wheels operate the smooth rise-and-fall and tilt. A slower gearing on the rise-and-fall would help when setting up; the calibration on the tilt is a useful setting guide.

The cast aluminium fence guard is well designed and robust; the easy to replace ply-

wood cheeks snag on their bolts but should free up with use.

Calibrations set into the bed are also a useful reference when setting the fence guard. A micro adjuster on the left-hand side has just the right amount of movement for setting a fine offset between the fences; large knobs lock everything securely.

Shaw guard assembly

Loosening two sliding knobs allows the shaw guard assembly to be swung up out of the way to give good access to the block.

The shaw guard, which holds wood into the fence, has a right-angle in its bracket that looks as if the bend was achieved by being stamped on with a heavy boot.

The switchgear to the left of the operating position includes an on- and off-switch and three illuminated selected spindle speed indicators.

A large door on the front gives good access for changing speeds, but a fussy C bracket has to be moved with the belt to illuminate the correct speed lamp.

No vibration

The machine runs quietly and with no vibration, but at the top speed of 8,700rpm care must be taken to ensure the cutter block can take it – a cutter flying around the workshop at an obscene speed will do more damage than a bullet.

When the self-braking motor is switched off the spindle stops quickly, releasing the brake and allowing the block to be swung by hand for setting up – making sure power is isolated first.

The good selection of spacers on the spindle provides for many

BELOW: Neat flip-up guard.

BELOW RIGHT: Tilting arbor unusual and useful.

different widths of block; the machine is also equipped with spacing discs for tenoning.

Three removable inserts in the bed ensure work is supported as much as possible whatever diameter block is used. A centre plug fills the last hole left by the inserts when sawing.

Sliding carriage

The light, virtually all-aluminium sliding carriage mounts onto the machine by means of another aluminium extrusion capped with a steel bar; this takes the weight of the carriage and the wood; although the operation of the carriage isn't that smooth there is no unwanted slack.

The fence can be angled up to 45° either way; a calibration for angles is set in the bed, but the (not very accurate) reading is taken from the back of the mounting bracket.

A block of wood fixes to the business end of the fence to safeguard blade and fence, the other end extending to allow the full width of cut.

The flip-over stop is interchangeable with that on the saw's mitre fence, which means they can both be used on either fence. Two lengths can thus be set – a bit 'Mickey Mouse' but better than nothing.

The rigid hold-down clamp has to be screwed the length of its thread to clamp stock; a tool-post and cam-clamp design would be better.

Planer-thicknesser

The supporting cabinet underneath the planer-thicknesser is in heavy gauge, pressed steel with a lumpy Hammerite-type coating. ➤

SPECIFICATIONS

SPINDLE/SAW/SLIDING CARRIAGE
Price: £2223 excluding VAT

Overall table size:	575 x 1135mm, 22⁵/₈ x 44³/₄in
Working height:	850mm, 33¹/₂in
Weight:	165kg, 363lb

SPINDLE
Maximum tool height:	110mm, 4¹/₄in
Arbor diameter:	30mm
Speeds:	4,800, 6,400, 8,700rpm
Maximum foward tilt:	30°
Maximum backward tilt:	5°

SAW
Distance between blade and fence	
Without extension table:	290mm, 11¹/₂in
With extension table:	890mm, 35in
Depth of cut:	85mm, 3³/₈in
Depth of cut at 45°:	55mm, 2¹/₈in
Blade speed:	4,100rpm
Blade diameter:	250mm, 10in
Tilt angle:	90° to 45°

SLIDING CARRIAGE
Table size:	500 x 210mm, 19³/₄ x 8¹/₄in
Stroke:	1350mm, 53¹/₈in
Length of fence:	1600mm, 63in
Fence angles:	45° - 0° - 45°

PLANER-THICKNESSER 638
Price: £1482 excluding VAT

SURFACER
Planing width:	310mm, 12¹/₄in
Table length:	1550mm, 61in
Block diameter:	80mm
Maximum cut:	4mm, ⁵/₁₆in
Speed:	5,850rpm

THICKNESSER
Maximum thickness:	230mm, 9in
Maximum cut:	4mm, ⁵/₁₆in
Feed speed:	7.5m/min, 24.6ft/min
Table length:	655mm, 25³/₄in

MORTISER 2653
Price: £391.92 excluding VAT

Table size:	400 x 200mm, 15³/₄in x 8in
Chuck capacity:	2.5 to 16mm, 3³/₂ to ⁵/₈in
Max length of mortise:	125mm, 5in
Max width of mortise:	16mm, ⁵/₈in
Height adjustment:	90mm, 3¹/₂in

MOTORS
Saw:	
Single or three phase:	1.5kw, 2hp
Spindle:	
Single or three phase:	1.5kw, 2hp
Planer-thicknesser	
Single phase:	1.8kw, 2.5hp
Three phase:	2.2kw, 3hp

● *For information on these and a large range of other machines and accessories and your nearest stockist contact Stayer Power Tools, Unit 9, Guildford Industrial Estate, Guildford, Surrey GU2 5YT, tel 01483 454502, fax 01483 454415.*

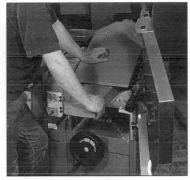

This structure is strong enough to support the beds and the heavy work sections being fed through.

The tables are both long and wide, providing good capacity for all but the most demanding users.

The dark finish alloy castings are very much a Kity hallmark and are well made, ground true and reliable to work on.

Noise reduction slots are incorporated and both tables are raised and lowered with large, stiff handgrip knobs.

The metric scale on the in-feed doesn't make sense to me and should be double-checked with a test cut.

Anodised fence

The fence is a long, heavy, anodised section with evil sharp ends; commendably, it is fitted to a heavy cast sliding piece running in a dovetailed keyway.

Angling of the fence operates in such a way as to avoid a nasty gap under the fence when bevel planing.

The guard is an assemblage of anodised aluminium which can be swung off the table by means of a snap-down lever.

A knob at the base of the

LEFT: Two machines, two testers.

CONCLUSION

TO call this a combination machine is not entirely accurate as it is really two machines.

Besides being easier to arrange in the workshop, their separation means more switch control; but the different fuses could make life difficult if spares aren't kept.

We have our reservations as to the longevity of the aluminium beds as the nice grey finish already has signs of wear.

But we like the versatile arrangement of this machine and believe it would be suitable for the furnituremaker with a smaller workshop.

guard arm sets the height clearance; the guard itself is a piece of curved alloy which can be adjusted to cover more or less of the cutterblock.

Thicknessing

Setting up for thicknessing entails firstly removing the entire fence arm assembly – which is a pain – and then unlocking the two table clamps.

These drop down out of the way allowing the tables to be swung up and the extraction hood to be pulled over the cutterblock and feed assembly.

The long tables have the projecting guard's arm at one end as well as being hinged at an angle, thus forming quite an obstacle to running round safely to collect work at the out-feed end!

Each table has a small – and useless – bonnet-type stay; if they did work they would invite a fragile pinkie to be crushed near the hinge knuckle while unlatching them!

A table-actuated switch on the outfeed side isolates the on-button used while overhanding.

The user should check each time that the spring clip which holds the extraction hood down over the block has engaged.

Lifting the hood reveals both the cutterblock and the drive mechanism.

This is a plain drive with a splined in-feed and plain out-feed roller. The well made cutter block is of the safety, triple knife-type which provides a good finish.

Anti kick-back teeth are fitted for user protection. The thicknessing bed is of good old-fashioned ground cast iron on a single fat, machined column with a large, easy to turn handwheel for smooth height changing.

The metric scale is easy to read, although the indicator lacks proper adjustment for calibration.

On-off switching consists of

large rubber-booted NVR devices at the thicknesser end with an isolator underneath, and smaller buttons at the top of the other end for overhand working.

Slot mortiser

To use the add-on slot mortiser it is necessary to unbolt a panel inside the thicknesser to remove part of the external fascia where the attachment then sits; also added inside are a reinforcement plate and four bolt-on dowels on the side of the planer's cabinet.

The mortiser is a tall, fairly heavy, folded steel affair with a wheel on its base for manoeuvrability.

Two scalloped knobs are employed to screw and lock it into place, but first a chuck housing on the end of the planer shaft must be removed in order to attach the chuck.

This fits into a plain socket and is held on by an Allen bolt; then the cover is refitted. Once the mortiser is mounted, the work can be raised and lowered by a handwheel. Two long levers operate the lateral movement and stop collars set the required dimensions.

The lever action isn't the smoothest, particularly the transverse. The screw-down work-clamps do their job although a clash of knobs and levers can occur mid stroke! A nice touch is an internal dust extraction pipe with a port near the base.

Chatter-free finish

The planer-thicknesser can handle heavy stock and gives a good, pretty much chatter-free finish for both surfacing and thicknessing. Extraction is efficient.

The slot mortiser is not a stunner, but then they never are – better to put your money towards something like the Sedgewick chisel mortiser, also tested in this issue. ∎

Kity 639 planer-th

Technical Editor **Alan Goodsell** powers up
to a three-phase machine

A FEELING OF déjà vu
swept over me when
extracting from its crate
the first Kity 639 to be seen in
the UK. The reason? The 639
is almost identical to the planer-
thicknesser part of the Kity
K310 Ti combination machine
tested on pp. 70-73, but larger.
The 639 can, in fact, be selected
as part of the higher specification K400 combination machine.

The 639 is available only in
three-phase, which may
eliminate it from the shopping
list of makers without the necessary power option - unless the
extra investment of a single to
three-phase power converter is
made.

Construction

The Kity's construction is a
mixture of the old and the new.
It doesn't fall into the pressed
steel and extruded aluminium
bolted together category, but
its conventional design
does make extensive use
of modern materials.

The surface beds are cast-
aluminium with a dark anodised
finish. They are light-weight,
straight and true, but scratches
in the finish of the machine I
tested posted a durability
warning even before use.

In readiness for the extra
forces that it will encounter,
the thicknessing bed, however,
is more substantially made

from cast-iron.

A heavy fabricated-steel cabinet supports the beds, extruded
aluminium fence and guards.

Bed operation

The beds are nice and long at
1630mm (64⅛in), with a
smooth, milled surface. They
are also wide but, although
measuring 460mm (18in) at
their extremities, the capacity
for machining is limited to
400mm (16in).

Both the outfeed and infeed
beds are height adjustable, the
outfeed so that it can be set
level with the cutters after a
knife change and the infeed so
that the depth of cut can be set.

Slackening the table clamps and rotating the beds' respective plastic handgrips has them moving smoothly and precisely. An extra lock holds the outfeed bed firmly in place.

Well-thought-out gearing means precise cuts can be set on the infeed bed, and although the calibration scale on the side looks a bit vague it is in fact quite accurate. Lining up the '1' mark on the bed with the '1' mark on the cabinet results in a cut of 1mm and so on.

Noise reduction slots on both beds ease the resonance of the cutterblock knives passing in close proximity to the bed edges – a common annoyance on planers without this facility.

Extraction is well catered for; dust is efficiently taken away into an extractor hood which sits under the surface beds when surface planing.

"It struck me later that I may have been sent the guard from the smaller 638 by mistake"

Guards, fences

The bridge guard is one of the off-the-shelf types often seen on new machines, and simply bolts to the side of the outfeed bed.

The assembly works well although the knob with which the guard height is adjusted is rather small. The aerofoil-shaped guard is ideal for a hand to slide over, and the whole assembly can easily be flipped back out of the way if necessary.

Setting the bridge guard exposed a few problems though. It is too short to reach right across the bed with the fence set right back, so leaving a 100mm (4in) gap.

It can only be wound up to allow timber 64mm (2in) thick to pass under it. This seems to

be at odds with the 639's 230mm (9in) thicknessing capacity although it struck me later that I may have been sent the guard from the smaller 638 by mistake.

The parallel fence is an elaborate, sturdy but carelessly finished aluminium extrusion with nasty sharp corners on each end, one of which took a lump of flesh out of my arm – don't worry Kity, I won't be suing this time!

Its mounting bracket enables the fence to be easily set at any angle between 0° and 45°. Adjustable stops fitted at both these extremities set these positions exactly; once this is done the fence can be quickly set to either one.

As the fence is positioned across the bed its slide covers the cutterblock. Unfortunately, even when locked tightly with the long lever, lateral play on the fence lets down this otherwise well-made assembly.

A debatable bonus is the machine's ability to take the Kity slot morticer accessory. Fitted onto the side of the cabinet, it is driven by the cutterblock shaft.

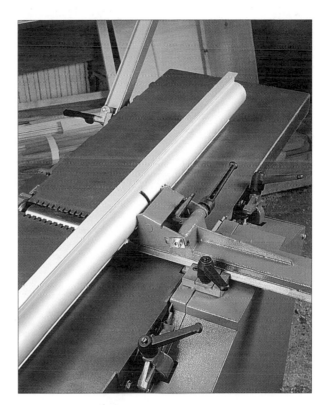

Thicknessing

To convert the 639 into thicknessing mode, be prepared for a lengthy process.

Firstly, the parallel fence must be slackened and swung out of the way, then the bridge guard is flipped over to the end of the outfeed bed. With this accomplished, the table clamps are slackened and swung down out of the way so that the beds,

ABOVE! Fence easily set for 90° and 45°; it managed to damage the tester, though

BELOW: Infeed bed adjustment and scale – surprisingly ➤ accurate

TOP: For thicknessing the beds are flipped up, exposing the cutterblock which is then covered by an extraction hood

ABOVE: Set up for thicknessing, the Kity is a bulky machine to get round

BELOW: Thicknessing bed is cast-iron – note substantial ram

hinged on the opposite side, can be lifted to just beyond vertical.

As the beds are raised, small, fiddly, bonnet hood-type catches drop into place to prevent the beds falling back down; lifting these returns the beds to horizontal.

Finally, the extractor hood is swung over into position, to be secured by an ineffective spring clip. Gravity does a better job.

While doing all this flipping and swinging I couldn't help thinking of those Transformer toys by which a robot turns into a car or suchlike; I hoped that if I swung or flipped just a few more things, the Kity might turn into a

Ferrari. Wishful thinking, but at least the machine – taking up twice as much space as before – was now ready for thicknessing.

Rise-and-fall

A large plastic wheel operates the single pillar rise-and-fall. The motion is smooth and well-geared for precise cuts. A large ratchet lever locks the bed firmly in position and a tin pointer positioned against a calibration accurately sets depth.

Although a single motor powers both the cutterblock and feed, a pull of a lever engages and disengages the feed. By means of a strangely complicated belt-and-pulley system another lever selects one of two different feed speeds.

Switchgear

What a treat! It's good to see that someone has gone to the trouble of working out exactly the correct sites for switches. Dust-proof, the on- and off-switches are well placed at both the surfacing and thicknessing operating positions.

A further locking mains isolating switch is provided for safety; a rather excessive bank of five fuses sits next to it.

The switches are all good quality; their positioning eliminates the temptation to lean over a running machine – or the nowadays-common long walk around it.

In use

The 3kW (4hp) three-phase motor runs smoothly, with more than adequate power to cope with both the cutterblock and the extensive belt-and-pulley feed system.

When surfacing, the three knife block produces a creditable finish on a selection of timbers of various widths. The fence is easily set; although it wobbles a bit laterally it remains firm at the angle set, allowing the achievement of square edges on timber.

Thicknessing also produces good results, and the ability to select different feed speeds increases the 639's ability to produce pleasing finishes on a variety of timbers and widths.

The single pillar rise-and-fall is sturdy and wobble-free, but for single-handed operation the process of thicknessing is hindered by the long walk around all the swung-out parts to take off.

Conclusion

The Kity 639 is well-designed and the ergonomics are sensibly thought out apart from the lengthy procedure when converting to thicknessing.

This machine is ideal for the maker who sometimes has to plane large section timber. The price tag is hefty, though, and the three-phase-only option could affect sales figures.

FACTS AND FIGURES

Price	£3,134 including VAT
Length of planer tables	1630mm (64⅛in)
Surface width	400mm (16in)
Thicknessing height	230mm (9in)
Diameter of cutterblock	80mm (3⅛in)
Speed of cutterblock	5850rpm
Number of cutters	3
Feed speeds	5.8m (19ft) per minute
	7.5m (24½ft) per minute
Motor	3kW (4hp)
Weight	300kg (660lbs)

● Availability: contact Stayer Power Tools, Unit 9, Guildford Industrial Estate, Guildford, Surrey GU2 5YT, tel 01483 454502, fax 01483 454415.

Workhorse for a lo

Technical Editor **Alan Goodsell** tries out the Rojek MSP 310 planer/thicknesser

RIGHT: Side covers are easily removed to give good access to the inner workings

BELOW: This planer/thicknesser is compact and affordable

AFTER THE sawbench the planer/thicknesser is probably the next most essential static machine purchase for a furniture-maker's workshop.

The ideal requirements for a planer/thicknesser are that it should be sturdy, easy to use and have surface beds that are as long as possible, to enable truing up of lengthy pieces of timber prior to thicknessing.

The Czech-built Rojek MSP 310 offered by Jordan Woodmachinery is a compact machine as well as being one of the lower-priced models available, so I thought it should be well worth checking out.

At F&C we usually try to test single-phase equipment, but due to a high demand for these machines only a three-phase version was available. As both the options give similar power specifications, however, they should perform almost identically.

Construction

The most distinctive feature of this machine is its boxy appearance. The steel cabinet is functional and unfussy due to its economical design. The side panels are easily removed and give unparalleled access to the inner workings for inspection and maintenance.

Cast-iron beds aren't the most substantial but they are precision-milled to a perfectly flat surface.

The machine arrives fully assembled on a pallet and is heavy enough to need a couple of colleagues to help shift it into place. All that needs fixing to it is the switchgear. Unusually, this is bolted to the side of the out-feed bed.

The scrappy photocopied manual gives some tips on planing procedures for the newcomer to woodworking, but extracting much more information from it is difficult.

The beds

Precision-milled, cast-iron beds on a lower budget machine are good to see — even though they are a slight compromise of functionality and economy they are still far preferable to the aluminium or pressed steel affairs offered by other manufacturers.

They could be longer, but that would alter the compact nature of the machine; they could be slightly sturdier, but that would push up the cost. In reality they are sturdy enough and long enough for the market the

wer budget

"Handy plastic triangular plates on the ends of the fence lay on the bed when the fence is angled, making the job of setting an angle of 45° easier"

machine is pitched at, so Rojek have got it spot on.

The infeed bed is adjusted for height by turning a knob on the end of the bed. The action is smooth and precise but the guide for setting the depth of cut consists of a chiselled-in mark on the bed that is supposed to line up with a peeling off calibration sticker on the cabinet. This is a joke and is impossible to use.

The outfeed bed has no adjustment for height so the cutters have to be set to it rather than set to each other, then the bed adjusted to them. However, being fixed does keep costs down and means there is one less mechanism to maintain.

To take the extra pressure to which it will be subjected, the thicknessing bed is more substantial than the surface beds. The rise-and-fall is of the single pillar type and is driven by a long inverted tooth belt. Although the action is a little agricultural the movement is precise, enabling accurate settings to be achieved.

The long metal rise-and-fall locking lever interferes with the plastic winding wheel, but in practice the lever needs only a small amount of movement to lock the bed securely in place. A calibration scale is provided to set the thickness and, once the tin pointer on the thicknessing bed is bent closer to it, it provides a surprisingly accurate guide.

I particularly liked the lack of need to flip up the surface beds to gain access to the thicknessing operation, meaning that the machine is always ready to use for either surfacing or thicknessing.

Fences, guards

The aluminium extruded fence is large and can be set at any angle from vertical to 45°. Two large ratchet levers on the simple but effective mounting lock it firmly in position, where it stays with no unwanted movement.

A small adjusting grub screw bears on the back of the fence to ensure that when returned to vertical it will be positioned at

exactly 90° to the bed. Handy plastic triangular plates on the ends of the fence lay on the bed when the fence is angled, making the job of setting an angle of 45° easier.

The fence slides smoothly across the machine and is locked in position with a small knob. The blade cover is also easily set but, in common with the fence, the small coarsely threaded locking knobs tend to vibrate loose.

The dust extractor hood is a natty dual purpose design. For thicknessing it sits on the surface beds and bolts to the fence; unfortunately this tends to crush the hollow fence when tightened.

For surface planing, the hood is slid on top of the thicknessing bed into the machine to a marked line, the thicknessing bed then being wound up to hold the hood in place.

Switchgear

The position of the switchgear is badly thought out. It is fixed to the outfeed bed via a piece of bent steel plate and juts precari- ➤

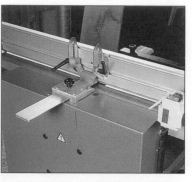

ously above the bed begging to be bashed off with a misguided piece of wood.

Even worse, when surface planing the operator has to either walk around the machine to switch it both on and off, or more likely succumb to the temptation of leaning over a running cutterblock.

This is a shame as the switch is a good one with no-volt release, overload protection and a lockable flap to prevent prying fingers starting the machine without authorisation.

Both these problems could be easily resolved by placing the switches in the centre of the side panel bearing the Rojek sticker. This would enable the operator to control the machine safely from both the surface planing and thicknessing positions.

In case anyone has examined the three-phase plug and wondered what the fifth pin is for, it is the link to activate the electronic brake on the motor. Rest assured the single-phase model also has a motor brake.

In use

The 2.2kW (3hp) motor runs well, with plenty of power to take some hefty use. The infeed and outfeed rollers are permanently engaged so when thicknessing, if a large cut slows the cutterblock too much, or a piece of wood becomes jammed — not an infrequent occurrence on

thicknessers — the only option is to switch off hurriedly and retrieve the drive-mangled piece of wood.

Large anti kick-back dogs perform well on both large and small section timber.

Surface planing produced true and square results and, due to the compact size of the machine, a lot of legwork is avoided.

The good quality four-knife

cutterblock produces a splendid finish on most timbers; when thicknessing a healthy 5mm (^{3}/$_{16}$in) cut can be taken.

Conclusion

The MSP 310 is ideally sized and priced for the serious amateur, a one-man furniture-maker with a smaller workshop, and would also serve well in a larger commercial workshop.

It is well built for the money and should prove to be a sturdy workhorse for many years.

With the simplicity of its design and construction the Rojek can easily be maintained by its owner.

A number of accessories are available, including table extensions, wheels to make it easier to shift around and an optional slot morticer attachment that could also prove useful for those with a shortage of space.

● *Available from:* Jordan Woodmachinery Ltd, Unit 6B, Philadelphia Complex, Houghton-le-Spring, Tyne & Wear DH4 4UG, tel 0191 5840784, fax 0191 5842973. ■

FACTS AND FIGURES

PRICES

MSP 310, both power options	£1252 including VAT
Slot morticing attachment	£321 including VAT
Maximum timber capacity	310 x 200mm (12 x 7^3/$_4$in)
Length of surfacer tables	1270mm (50in)
Diameter of cutterblock	106mm (4^1/$_8$in)
Speed of cutterblock	4300rpm
Number of cutters	4
Maximum stock removal, thicknessing	5mm (^{3}/$_{16}$in)
Feed speed	5m/min (16ft/min)
Motor power, three-phase	2.2kW (3hp)
Motor power, single-phase	2.2kW (3hp)
Weight	280kg (620lb)

Heavyweight

Anthony Bailey puts power to his elbow testing six ¹/₂in collet routers costing under £450 including VAT, recommended retail price

▲ *A 'plunge' of heavyweight routers. (If readers have a better collective name for routers, please let me know - Ed.) The greyed-out monsters are tested in part two, on pages 94-97*

For anyone with a long-term, serious interest in routing, these muscular machines offer immense power and the capability to take up to ¹/₂in shank cutters. This impressive show of strength also makes possible a wider range of profiles.

Invert one in a table and the sort of large and difficult machining operations that might normally be tackled by a spindle moulder can be carried out by a router instead.

SKIL 1875U1

This comfortable, well-balanced router has integrated handgrips and motor housing. The textured grips function well. An effective sprung switch trigger and on-lock are fitted to the right-hand grip. The spanner for cutter-changing is securely held on top of the motor. The end of the large steel-plate spindle lock is rolled over for comfort.

The collet nut has the collet machined into it, and the entire nut must be exchanged for other collet sizes.

The shaped, textured-plastic plunge lever is pressed down to lock. The return springing is not that positive although motor vibration helps it back.

£316

▲ *SKIL 1875U1*

s in the ring

"The gaitered plunge columns look snazzy but don't really serve a proper function — unless you really want to grease the columns liberally and avoid dust mixing with it!"

▼ *HITACHI M12SA*

▲ *FREUD FT2000VCE*

The depth stop rod is locked by a knob at the side which causes a clash of fingers and housing. Another small knob locks the sliding plastic depth setting blade, and the depth stop turret is easy to turn.

The baseplate sits in a protective plastic container rather than having the more usual Tufnol covering. It incorporates a chipping deflector and provision for a dust spout. A clear plastic adapter holds guide bushes. A tiny little side fence that has to be locked with a screwdriver can be fitted — extension facings can be attached. The fine adjuster doesn't work too well either.

On test
The efficient motor operates smoothly, even though it does try to move away when you switch on. Speed changing is constant.

FREUD FT2000VCE
The stable Freud has long, comfortable hand grips. The top-mounted speed control is easy to turn, and although the on-off switch is on the body, rather than more conveniently on a hand-grip, it is fairly easy to operate.

The gaitered plunge columns look snazzy but don't really serve a proper function — unless you really want to grease the columns liberally and avoid dust mixing with it!

The plunge lock lever at the back flicks on and off easily and is nicely biased to the unlocked position. The plunge return is

limited by a slow wind knob, fitted for convenience when the router is inverted.

During heavy machining the knob, which is a loose-running fit, can vibrate downwards and unintentionally limit the return height.

A firmly sprung depth stop lock button releases the threaded stop rod, but some effort is needed to move it. On top of the rod is a clear plastic magnifier with a line which sets against a dual metric/imperial scale. The three-stage depth stop turret turns easily.

The smooth baseplate accepts a chippings deflector and spout. A range of guide bushes can also be fitted.

The fixed rods of the skimpy, bent metal side fence cut down its usefulness. The fine adjuster isn't so good when moving the fence in, but works well enough when winding out.

On test
Apart from the slightly scratchy sounding bearings, the Freud delivers a lot of power efficiently.

HITACHI M12SA
This is the non-electronic version of Hitachi's big and stable router. The comfortable hand-grips have a useful grip pattern. ▶

◄ MAKITA 3612BR

> "Although chunky and heavy, the Makita is a compact and stable no-frills piece of kit"

It has easy brush cover access and a snap-on-and-off switch operated by the thumb.

The depth stop rod is uniquely Hitachi. A knob on the side is rotated to move the rod up and down via cogged toothing. Pulled outwards it moves the scale in a similar fashion. Both the scale and the rod have their own lock knobs.

The easy to turn depth stop turret has one fixed and two adjustable stages.

The plunge action works well, but the lock is a rather uncomfortable piece of pressed steel, which operates in a vertical position and tends to dig into the fingers.

Although the spindle lock is off to the side next to one plunge column, access is not difficult and cutters are easily changed.

The collet and nut are of one piece, with spanner flats machined onto the end.

The neatly cast baseplate takes guide bushes. The side fence has adjustable rods which lock firmly in place via neat lock knobs. It also incorporates an efficient fine adjuster.

On test
Apart from a bit of a kick on start-up, the noisy motor stays even in note.

MAKITA 3612BR
Although chunky and heavy, the Makita is a compact and stable no-frills piece of kit. With no electronics fitted, expect an arm-wrenching torque reaction on start-up. The old-fashioned on-off switch lever is rather stiff and uncomfortable.

The brush access covers are on the outside. The pressed steel plunge lock lever on the well-shaped handgrips falls easily to hand, but is uncomfortably close to the right handgrip, so your fingers get stuck between the two.

The plunge action is very springy and one column has a plastic nut to limit the height return.

A heavily sprung brass button locks the threaded depth stop rod and a plastic milled knob on the top can be turned for fine adjustments against a metric scale — a little awkward to use but quite effective and secure.

The turret stop is easy to turn and the baseplate is a streamlined casting without dust traps. A chippings deflector and guide bushes can be fitted.

The side fence is short, with fixed rods and the fine adjuster works reasonably well but a little stiffly.

The side fence can be replaced by a roller guide for working along uneven edges or profiles. Pressing a button locks the spindle for one-spanner cutter-changing.

On test
Without electronic control, the Makita tried to pull my arm from it's socket, but motor noise was average, maintaining an even note with loads of power.

BOSCH 1600A
The Bosch stands tall. Although quite heavy, it is comfortable to hold, with well-shaped handgrips. One incorporates a well-sprung switch trigger and a small off-lock for safety.

The plunge lock is an outsize silvered casting with a shaped end and a long throw to the side when unlocking it. The plunge return springing works well but is a little sluggish unless the lock is pulled right down.

The crude depth stop rod has a clear plastic flag engraved with a line for the metric/imperial depth settings. This rod waggles loosely when undone and falls out very easily. The plunge height return limiting rod has two plastic nuts for setting both minimum and maximum height, although the former setting seems a little pointless.

A tall chip deflector shields the cutter. A small projection running behind the turret begs to get snapped off.

Guide bushes are held in by tall milled knobs and bolts. The fence lock knobs lack anti-vibration springs, one of them tending to clash with the chip deflector and the lower nut on the height return rod.

The rigid plastic fence has separate rods and a rather stiff fine adjuster.

On test
This very smooth motor tends to pull away, but is reasonably powerful.

"A small projection running behind the turret begs to get snapped off"

▲ BOSCH 1600A

RYOBI RE 601

This new router is well balanced and easy to hold due to the nice long handgrips, one with an integral on-off switch with safety locking.

The plunge lock is comfortable to use, and the good plunge action is complemented by adequate return springing. The plunge columns are fashionably gaitered and a wraparound chippings deflector is fitted at the front.

The integral fine depth adjuster is excellent. It doesn't try to adjust of its own accord when machining, so is very suitable for inversion work. It offers a choice of speeds and a natty geared depth adjuster which is a touch waggly but very useable, while the three-stage turret has remarkably short bolts giving rather limited stage depth cutting.

The baseplate is entirely round in the American fashion, making it harder to use against a straight guide fence, though not impossible. It has the facility to fit normal guide bushes.

The skimpy side fence with fixed rods can take wooden fac-

ings and the fine adjuster works creditably well.

On test

The very smooth and relatively quiet motor marks out this machine as a thoroughly modern, well bred router.

ROUND TWO

All these heavyweight routers should give adequate service, although inevitably some shine more than others. You'll find my judge's verdict in part two, on pages 94-97, where I report on the next bout, between heavyweights costing more than £450 including VAT. ●

■ **N.B. All recommended retail prices are inclusive of VAT. See pages 114-115 for Router Specifications and Contacts.**

▲ RYOBI RE 601

Mafell LO 50E ar

£229

TESTER

Anthony Bailey

Anthony Bailey tests two Mafell routers – and finds welcome similarities to Festo models and some good features of their own

MAFELL LO 50E

THE top cover of the LO 50E is flattened, and while 'palm-gripping' onto its slightly ridged pattern is not so comfortable, the machine can be inverted when cutter changing.

A fine adjuster tip is located at the bottom end of the depth stop rod which sets against a metric scale. The turret

stop turns easily but is mounted on a base that lacks built-in extraction.

There is, however, an add-on spout as well as a screw-in guide bush. The on/off trigger switch favours right-handers, and a wheel has six speed wheel settings that range from 10,000 to 22,000rpm.

The rather large scalloped plunge lock knob resembles that of its big brother, and has an anti-vibration spring, as do the other angular-shaped fence lock knobs.

The simple side fence has neither extraction bowl nor adjustable faces, but does have a workable fine adjuster.

On test

At 2.7kg, this model is heavy but is well balanced, with a comfortable grip. I expected it

▲ *The Mafell LO 50E looks familiar*
◄ *The side fence on the LO 50E has an effective fine adjuster*

"I expected it to behave like a Festo on power up and wasn't disappointed"

to behave like a Festo on power up and wasn't disappointed. These 900W machines are pleasant to use because the motors are so smooth and quiet, and speed-changing is instantaneous – a joy indeed.

The plunge stroke is 50mm (2in), but the action is a little less than silky although the springing appears to have been upped to counteract this.

The extraction spout works properly on what is a well-behaved machine.

£435

MAFELL LO 65E

THE speed change wheel on this bigger machine scales from 8 to 20, representing 8,000 to 20,000rpm rather than a single number scale as on the small machine. The rocker-type on/off switch has taken an ergonomic step backwards, and is located on the front where it is just a little hard to reach, especially as the on-position is shielded for safety.

Instead of a plunge lock lever the right-hand knob is turned; this has a better feel, and is aided by the scalloping of the comfortable knobs.

The depth stop rod is identical to the smaller model, but the turret stop is unaccountably stiff to turn – although it will probably loosen up after use.

The return rod on the top right has a single thumbwheel to set the stop and could do with another to lock it in place.

The baseplate lacks a smooth top surface, so providing plenty of dust traps. The underside, however, has a shiny stainless steel facing rather than the more usual phenolic resin sheet.

A protective plastic coating is hard to remove, and reveals a nice-looking surface which is a bit vulnerable to scratching.

Guide bushes can be fitted to the baseplate. Its two long, flat sides are useful for working against a straight-edge. Usefully long fence rods are supplied, and the side fence has a proper fine adjuster.

Cutter changing requires the use of one spanner and depression of a small domed lock button; the supplied 8mm collet is a high quality item.

On test

The LO 65E is heavy at 5.5kg and tall, but it is very stable. Like the small machine it is quiet and smooth, with even speed changing. The plunge stroke is 65mm (2½in), its action being very efficient, with good springing and comfortable grip knobs. There is plenty of power at the cutting edge for heavy duty working.

▲ *The Mafell LO 65E is tall but very stable*
▶ *The LO 65E has an unusual stainless steel facing on the baseplate*

Conclusion

This brace of Mafells are essentially 'down engineered' Festos, providing the chassis and engine of a Mercedes, but finished off to Volkswagen Beetle standard.

Mafell have added their own input to produce two routers with world-class motors for a distinctly down-engineered price.

See pages 114-115 for Router Specifications and Contacts.

Prices are recommended retail and include VAT ●

Choose yo

TESTER:
Anthony Bailey

Anthony Bailey puts 10 small professional routers through their paces

R OUTERS in the 720W to 1100W power bracket are generally described by the term $^1/_4$in routers, although most will take collets between 6mm and the increasingly popular 8mm.

To reflect the greater loading being put on small routers, larger motors and electronics are more or less obligatory. Those tested are some of the newest on the market.

RYOBI RE 155 K

This brand new model is an example of the new breed of 8mm capacity machines. It has a collet insert for 1/4in cutters, a spindle lock for easy cutter changing and a low centre of gravity.

Large handgrips incorporate the thumbwheel for easy speed-setting, and the safety off-lock button. The depth stop rod, which could fall out when the router is upturned, is set against a metric scale.

The three-stage depth setting turret is easy to turn and sits on one corner of the base. The plunge springing is not quite as positive as some and the lever must be pressed well down for the lock to operate.

The base has fence locking knobs with anti vibration springs and a wide opening over which is bolted a clear plastic dust spout. Under it are threaded supports for

▲ *Ryobi RE 155 K*

guide bushes and two threaded holes for table mounting. The fence has fixed rods and no means of fine adjustment.

On test

The bulbous handgrips grew on me and the handling was good. The quiet and smooth motor changes speed quickly. The Ryobi coped well under load and extraction was adequate.

ATLAS COPCO OFS 720

This no-nonsense router has a lowish centre of gravity and comfortable grip knobs. The on/off switch favours left-handers like me, and has an unusual rocker action.

The easy to use geared rise-and-fall on the depth stop has a large knob with a resettable

ur weapon

metric scaled collar. Cutter changing requires just one spanner and the spindle lock. The plunge action is a bit sluggish, but the vibration of the motor returns it quickly.

The alloy-cast base has a three-stage turret and two fence lock knobs with anti vibration springs, plus a fitting position for the fine fence adjuster. The fence has adjustable rods and fairly short facings.

A dust spout and a guide bush can be fitted. Sadly there is no provision on the baseplate for table fixings.

On test

With no electronics to beef up the power when under load the Atlas Copco isn't as powerful as some. The drop in motor speed was noticeable when machining. Extraction was OK.

METABO OF E 1229 SIGNAL

For an expensive machine this one includes only a fence and dust spout, but does have some neat design features.

The speed control wheel is discreetly tucked away at the top of the cas-

£448

▲ *Metabo OF E 1229 Signal*

▲ *Atlas Copco OFS 720*

ing and the right-hand grip contains the slightly stiff on/off switch and the plunge lock. A dial gauge for depth setting is adjusted via a milled knob at the top of the depth rod. It gives precise settings. A scale on the depth rod side gives whole millimetre settings, while the dial is in 0.1mm increments. The three-stage turret has a high, milled base for easy turning, and a very positive ballbearing action.

Cutter changing is via a spindle lock although the flats on the collet nut are rather narrow. The plunge springing is good, with a rapid return stroke, but there is noticeable play on the body when the plunge lock is off.

"To reflect the greater loading being put on small routers, larger motors and electronics are more or less obligatory"

The straight-sided base has two springless fence lock knobs. Template guides can be bolted into place and a plastic dust spout passes over one fence rod.

The fence has fixed rods and a fine adjuster hidden inside the fence casting in the form of an alloy bar with two strong springs acting on it.

On test

Despite electronic control, the noisy Metabo still wanted to jump at start-up. Speed changing was hindered by the recessed

▲ *DeWalt 621*

thumbwheel, but the change was smooth and demonstrated good power under load. Extraction was satisfactory.

DEWALT 621

This competent heavy-duty piece of gear breaks the 1000W barrier, is identical except for colour to the ELU OF 97EK, and has built-in extraction and safety switching. The motor body is not excessively large and the electronic speed wheel is easy to turn. The large dust spout extracts through the larger of the two plunge columns and the end can be capped, swivelled or removed.

Soft rubber grip knobs make for better holding, the left one acting as a twist action plunge lock and the right incorporating the on/off switch and off-lock. The solid geared depth stop is moved easily by turning a large milled plastic knob. The lock knob features an anti vibration spring. A fine adjustment knob is too small for easy turning.

Below a large plastic ▶

▲ Bosch Gof 900 ACE

"The noise level off-load was quite bearable although serious machining sent the decibels up"

spindle lock button is a clear plastic vortex shield which aids extraction without loss of visibility.

The three-stage depth turret is firm to turn but does stay put. The pressed steel straight fence has a built-in and effective fine adjuster. It has its own extraction pipe and the rods are removable. Pressed steel template guides fit in the large baseplate opening, which also features two threaded holes for table mounting.

On test

It handles nicely and powers up smoothly, with very even speed changes and good extrac-

tion. The noise level off-load was quite bearable although serious machining sent the decibels up. The controls function well.

DEWALT 613

The 613 model, created as part of the original UK DeWalt line, has all the hallmarks of the earlier ELU MOF 96 series in terms of the base, knobs, scalloped handgrips and depth stop.

The motor casing is a rather different rounded shape with a casting at the bottom to match. In power terms the 800W motor produces a useful output for most purposes.

The plunge grip knob and the three-stage turret are stiff but the plunge action itself is smooth and has a rapid return.

DeWalt 613 ▶

The depth stop is basic but does work quite well, setting against a clear black and yellow scale.

The on/off switch is ridged, with an apex shape allowing it to be pushed or pulled. No electronics are fitted.

There is a large spindle lock and the DW 613 comes with a standard 1/4in collet. The base has two holes for table mounting and the clear plastic dust spout and template guides are held in place by machine screws and bolts. The familiar fence has anti vibration springs.

On test

Apart from the rather tight plunge lock knob and the depth turret, it performs well, with a smooth and unflustered motor. Large chippings tend to block the extraction pipe.

BOSCH GOF 900 ACE

Yet again Bosch have developed a high tech piece of hardware. The casing is large and wide. The right-hand of the comfortable and long handgrips incorporates the trigger switch and safety off-button. The heavily sprung, plastic plunge lever requires half-loosening your grip to reach it. The speed control dial is mounted on the front

and the built-in rise-and-fall knob unusually placed on the top. It is scaled in metric and imperial, and allows precise adjustment either in or out of a router table.

A clear plastic indicator is set against a scale, but easily slides off the effective little depth rod.

The turret stop turns easily and there is provision for a dust shield and extraction spout.

Bayonet template guide bushes are fitted by operating a sprung lever. The spindle lock is a swinging plate type and the fence a rather oversized affair with a stiff but effective fine adjuster.

On test

The Bosch stands still at switch-on, with a fractional delay in powering up, and speeds are changed quickly. Enough power is available for a rapid deep plunge and the revs stay even. A good reliable workhorse.

FESTO OF 900E

Festo's router has the same body casing as their orbital sander, sharing its simple squeeze trigger with an on-lock but no safety off-lock.

£252

▲ Hitachi M8

Remember not to squeeze the trigger when picking up the router.

The front knob acts as the plunge lock and the springing is positive. As you plunge, a metric scale disappears into the body to the depth set. The zero mark didn't line up with the scale but could be adjusted. A milled knob allows fine depth adjustment.

The spindle is locked by pushing a green button and the collet nut has just a narrow set of flats.

One major feature is the in-built extraction in the base, served by an oval dust port on the side.

The dust 'bowl' on the fence can be replaced by the excellent Festo guide rail system. An adjustable foot on the reverse allows the router to run level when the guide is in use.

On test

The Festo's quiet and smooth motor changes speed quickly up and down and copes well with a 'rough cut'. The built-in facility makes for good extraction. This fairly sophisticated machine is good to use on fine work.

HITACHI M8

This efficient-looking piece of kit and its electronic brother, the M8V, have been around for a while and display no fancy styling, just functional knobs and levers. The on/off switch needs only slight thumb pressure to move it up or down.

The depth setting is unusual, but involves setting the stop by operating a knob on the side, then unlocking the moveable scale by pulling out the same

knob. This scale can then be 'backed off' by the required amount for the plunge depth required.

The motor brushes are easily reached from the outside of the casing and underneath is a neat sideways-sliding spindle lock for cutter changing. The plunge lock lever is a flat piece of pressed steel with square edges. The alloy-cast base has an easily turned three-stage turret with fittings for a template guide and pressed steel fence with fixed rods. No extraction facility is supplied.

On test

Because the motor powers-up instantly, you need to hold on to the router. The level of noise becomes louder under load and the lack of extraction is a nuisance. ▶

▼ Hitachi M8V

£312

FESTO OF 900 E

◀ Festo OF 900 E

£319

HITACHI M 8V

◀ HITACHI M8V

Unlike most electronic models which have more power to copy with heavy loadings, this version operates on the same wattage as the similar M8. The casing is slightly higher on account of the electronics and the speed dial is rather awkwardly tucked away in the casing at the top.

The cast fence has loose rods and is supplied with a useful fine adjuster. Again, no dust spout is supplied.

On test

The M8V has an odd noise which can be felt as well as heard at switch-on. Compared to other electronic models the lack of extra power to boost torque under load was noticeable. Dust extraction would have been useful.

EINHELL EOF 850 SP

This router from Austria appears competently made and closely resembles the ELU MOF 96 series.

The scalloped knobs are encircled by an uncomfortable moulding, and the low-positioned switch, though easy to flick on, is difficult to turn off.

Einhell EOF ▶ 850 SP

The basic depth stop works fairly well, locking in position against a metric scale. All the small knobs have anti vibration springs.

The simple pressed steel spindle lock works smoothly and the 8mm nut and collet unit has a $\frac{1}{4}$in insert supplied for use in the UK.

The plunge action is smooth and the return spring strong.

The base has an easy to turn three-stage depth turret and appears identical to the MOF 96, so ELU accessories will fit.

Table mounting would require using the fence rods or fitting clamps.

A rather large 30mm guide bush and a dust spout are supplied.

The fence has built-in fine adjustment and a supplied trammel point fits onto a fence rod.

On test

For a bargain basement router it works well, with a quiet motor and a decent amount of power. The on/off switch is a nuisance, extraction is satisfactory, but the pipe can restrict large chippings. ●

Conclusion

All 10 tested performed at least averagely but four stand out.

Pick of the bunch are the big **DeWalt 621** with its smooth, powerful motor and a host of intelligent design features including extraction, and the **Festo OF 900 E** with its powerful, quiet motor, compact and unusual handling and in-built extraction system.

In second place is the **Bosch GOF 900 ACE** with its smart, modern design and plenty of power.

Lastly, the bargain of the lot, the **Einhell EOF 850 SP**, a hefty but workable machine.

. . . .

All prices quoted are inclusive of VAT.
See pages 114-115 for Router Specifications and Contacts.

Sumo wrestling supremos

In part two of his giant router tests **Anthony Bailey** muscles up to the sumo wrestlers of the group — $1/2$in collet monsters costing more than £450 including VAT, recommended retail price

As mentioned in part one (*see pages 82-85*), routers of this size and power are a must for those with a long-term, serious interest in routing. Inversion in a table brings them closer to their distant spindle moulder cousins.

HITACHI M12V

Apart from the fact that the M12V has electronic speed control and extra power to take advantage of it, this machine is virtually identical to the M12SA tested in TR2. Unfortunately, however, the speed setting wheel is recessed too far inside the top housing to be easy to turn.

Comfortable hand-grips have a useful grip pattern, and the neat, cast baseplate provides stability and takes guide bushes.

The body has easy brush cover access and a snap-on and -off switch operated by pressing the thumb up or down between two flanges.

A side knob operates the uniquely Hitachi depth stop via cogged toothing; pulling the knob outwards moves the scale, which, like the rod, has its own lock knob. The easy to turn turret has one fixed and two adjustable stages.

The vertically operating pressed steel plunge lock tends to dig into the fingers. Although the spindle lock is next to one plunge column, access

is not difficult.

The collet and nut are of one piece, with spanner flats machined onto the end. The fence has adjustable rods and a fine adjuster which works properly!

Apart from the higher casing, the only difference is not having your arm wrenched from its socket on start up! The straight fences are a bit short, although wood facings can be added to increase the running surface.

On test

The M12V is a powerful and controlled machine which starts smoothly and changes speed evenly.

"A side knob operates the uniquely Hitachi depth stop via cogged toothing"

£457

£462

▲ Atlas Copco OFSE 2000

▲ Hitachi M12V

◀ ATLAS COPCO OFSE 2000

Although bearing the Atlas Copco badge, this machine is essentially the same as the Freud FT2000VCE tested on page 83, but it has been downgraded slightly by missing off the fine depth adjuster.

This stable router has long, comfortable hand-grips, an easy to operate top-mounted speed control and body-mounted on-off switch.

Good-looking gaitered plunge columns offer protection, and the plunge lock lever at the back flicks on and off easily. Plunge return is limited by a slow wind knob which tends to vibrate downwards during heavy machining.

The baseplate will accept a chippings deflector and spout, and a range of guide bushes can also be fitted.

It comes with a heavy-duty pressed-steel case.

On test

The Atlas Copco behaves just like the Freud router — a big machine providing plenty of power for big work.

FESTO OF2000E PLUS

This Festo is solid, tall, reasonably well balanced, with large, comfortable, angled hand-grips. The slightly awkward power switch lever requires an amount of thumb pressure to switch on, but is easily switched off.

Plunging is good, but requires some effort due to the strong return spring. The plunge lock lever hangs down, is effortless to lock but can be unlocked only by exerting slightly uncomfortable knuckle pressure.

The electronic speed control is well positioned at the top of the housing, a handy chart on the front indicating cutter and material speeds.

The depth stop rod has a fine adjuster at the bottom, and is smoothly operated by a plastic tab; another tab features a blade edge for setting against the metric depth scale.

For more than normal locking positions the easy to use spindle lock engages with one of four holes in the spindle.

Lock knobs lacking anti-vibration springs secure a large side fence — equipped with a splendid fine adjuster — to the fence rod's unusual machined flats.

Guide bushes can be fitted via three screw holes; a useful chip deflector and dustspout are supplied.

On one base side there is provision for a compensating 'foot' to keep the router level when running on the Festo guide rail system.

On test

This model is very smooth at switch-on, and speed changing is also accomplished without fuss, demonstrating plenty of power.

DEWALT 625E

This model is almost identical to the ELU 177E which it succeeds; anyone who has used the ELU over the years will know that it is a reliable and standard industry workhorse.

The DeWalt stands quite high and is easy to handle, with good ergonomic hand-grips. The on-off switch mounted near the hand-grip is flicked on easily.

The plunge action is very springy and the comfortable lock lever works well. The speed dial is easy to turn, while cutter changing is a simple spindle lock and spanner job. The depth stop rod is geared, lockable and has a movable clear magnifier with a zero line for depth setting; a reasonably easy to turn three-stage turret is fitted to the base.

The baseplate is round with one straight running edge, and the supplied dustspout can be fitted, as can a series of guide bushes.

Side fence locking is achieved via knobs fitted with anti-vibration springs; as on the ELU, the fence's fine adjustment is disappointingly stiff to operate.

On test

Smooth powering up and very even speed-changing are slightly marred by a tendency to pull away a little.

£512

▲ **Festo OF 2000E Plus**

£535

▲ *DeWalt 625E*

METABO OFE 1812

Although tall, the Metabo is well balanced and incorporates some useful features, like nicely contoured hand-grips and a very easy to adjust speed dial.

The simple but effective geared depth rod has an adjustable metric-scaled collar for setting against a pointer. An easy to turn fine depth adjuster makes this model ideal for table inversion, even without proper base fixings.

A small orange slide lock protects the right-hand-grip's switch trigger; this must be pulled down before the trigger can be depressed. In spite of a hint of 'give', the plastic plunge lock lever works well.

There is a spindle lock button and the collet and nut are separate, the collet being nicely machined. The base has traps for chippings and dust to collect in, but at least it does have two long, flat running sides for working against a straight edge.

The 50mm cutter opening is limiting, but on the plus side guide bushes and a clip-on dustspout can be fitted.

The large side fence, fitted with a fine adjuster, has adjustable facings and long rods.

On test

The Metabo starts nicely, has a very bearable noise level, but is a little slow responding to speed changes. ▶

"The baseplate will accept a chippings deflector and spout, and a range of guide bushes can also be fitted"

£601

▲ *Metabo OFE 1812*

"Anyone who has used the ELU over the years will know that it is a reliable and standard industry workhorse"

CONCLUSION

Although some shine more than others, all the heavyweight routers I have tested should give adequate service. The Hitachis are nice to use and have decent fine fence adjustment. The Skil 1875U1 is also good, but let down by the poor little fence. The well-designed Metabo would come out as an outright winner, but for the baseplate with its smallish cutter opening and dust traps. The DeWalt is predictably useful and takes plenty of accessories, but again is a touch spoiled by a lack of attention at the manufacturing stage.

The Bosch and the Festo both have comprehensive ranges of system accessories and give a feeling of confidence in use. The Makita is basic but workable while the Copco/Freud models are both powerful and economically priced.

The Ryobi just about has it right, although the depth stop is not quite as neat as it could be.

My own personal favourites are the Festo OF 2000E Plus and the Ryobi RE 601, with the DeWalt 625E and Metabo OFE 1812 closely behind.

Router Specifications and Contacts are on pp. 114-115.

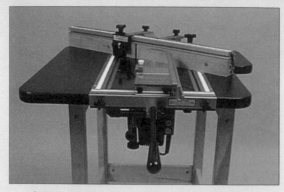

Rout-R-slide table

TESTER

Anthony Bailey

Anthony Bailey puts a router table offering a new approach to familiar problems through its paces

A NEW type of router table, claimed to be a revolutionary design and the complete router table system, is being imported from Jessum Products of Canada. Its North American origins show in the sort of precision engineering and gold anodising seen on other products from across the Atlantic.

Assembly

The ash underframe is fairly easy to put together, although having acquired a splinter when handling the components, I smoothed off the corners with sandpaper to make them nicer to handle.

Checking the base after assembly, I realised that adding a little glue to the joints would have been a good idea as only one barrel bolt and nut fix each piece together. They could work loose with the stresses of a routing session.

The table top and its sliding components are not too tricky to work out, and the accompanying photos are easy to understand.

How it works

Having successfully assembled the Rout-R-Slide, I watched the instructional video which shows the various joint-making possibilities.

The quality of the tape is rather poor, although a new one is apparently in the pipeline, but the presenter, who clearly knows the Rout-R-Slide inside out, imparted the gist of this tricky gadget.

The basic concept is that the work is held still while the router is pulled forward on rails under the table. This means that the workpiece can be held securely while cutting a range of joints; the fence swivels, allowing dovetails to be easily formed.

The sliding router and swivelling fence enable a whole series of other operations to

◀ *Once the router is fixed to the mounting plate the assembly is slid into the table*

▲ *The unusual Rout-R-Slide table*

be carried out, such as finger joints, housings, mortice and tenons, biscuit jointing – even board trimming.

Essentially the table is meant for jointing, although the router can be locked in position when mouldings are more conventionally run.

The sliding, phenolic resin mounting plate must be carefully drilled to take your router. This is then fixed to it with counter-sunk machine screws. Once attached, the plate, rollers and pull arm are lifted and slid into position under the table top; an aluminium extrusion on the front is fitted to hold all in place,

Two sliding and lockable collars on the pull arm determine backward and forward travel, and a strong lock lever on the front of the table allows the router to be fixed in position and remain static for certain operations.

The fence swivels about a fixed point in the bed and two bolts slide in channels running from front to back of the table.

▲ *Travel can be limited with two sliding and lockable collars; a strong lock lever fixes the router in position*

Two knobs on top tighten the fence at the angle set. A scale at the back of the fence gives precise degree settings and two adjustable nylon stops ensure repeatable settings.

There is some degree of forward and backward adjustment on the fence, and its facings can be adjusted or replaced with a through fence.

Handily, the black finished alloy stop is set with a pin locating in one of the holes on top of the left-hand half fence at 25mm (1in) intervals.

Its built-in fine adjusting wheel is extremely useful for in-between settings. The stop determines the spacings between pins and tails on joints, although for some, their spacings may be rather far apart.

A downside for we metricated Europeans is that the fence's scale is in imperial only.

Slotted extrusions at front and back of the table allow the fence to be swapped around so that the router runs lengthways

with the workpiece – making it ideal for mortice and tenons.

On test

When the fence is set at 15° the extraction port clashes with one of the nylon angle setting knobs – a pity as greater angles present no problem. I like the speed at which the fence can be set using all the scales provided.

The stop and pin for joint cutting are good, but the fine adjuster is a little awkward to turn. A perspex guard running almost the full length of the table is mounted at the front, and adjusts easily for safe but clear working.

The 'push me-pull you' cut action seems a little alarming, but the big guy on the video holds the work with one hand while moving the router with the other, so it must be OK.

In fact the rotation and pressure of the advancing cutter not only holds the work-

"The 'push me-pull you' cut action seems a little alarming, but the big guy on the video holds the work with one hand while moving the router with the other, so it must be OK"

piece in place but also pushes it against the stop – so don't set stops at positions to the right of the cutter as the work would pull away from them and possibly fly off the table!

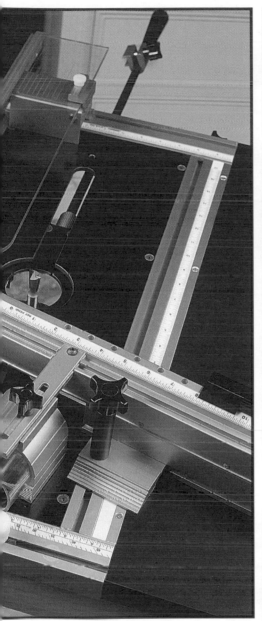

Facts and figures

Price	£425 including VAT plus delivery
Supplier	Everglades International Ltd.
Overall dimensions	700 by 762 by 844mm (27$\frac{9}{16}$ by 30 by 33$\frac{1}{4}$in)
Stroke capacity	340mm (13$\frac{1}{2}$in)
Weight	34kg (75lb)

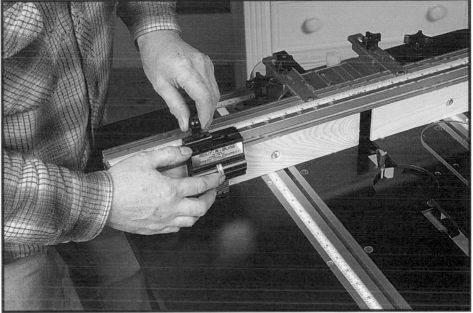

▲ A handy feature is the alloy stop which can be set at 25mm (1in) intervals

▲ The fence swivels about a fixed point in the bed and a scale at the back of the fence gives precise degree settings

The dovetail cutter was sharp, and both the push and return passes leave the wood in a neat, unsplintered condition, with successive passes giving a nice even result.

It goes without saying that a fine depth adjuster is needed in this or any table. Without one I was unable to cut joints like a mortice and tenon easily as the cutter has to be precisely wound up into the workpiece.

Conclusion

I liked this table a lot considering I'm not a gadget nut. I feel the lack of fine pitch spacing for dovetails and finger joints is a minus, although use of a packing piece may allow more options.

The Rout-R-Slide does offer a new approach to old problems, right down to cleanly trimming boards which, even with a good dimensioning saw, is difficult because of spelching.

The whole assembly takes up a pleasingly

▲ The fence can be turned around so that the router runs lengthways, making it ideal for mortice and tenons

small amount of space, yet offers a useful working table area with the capability of cutting many types of joint.

The video provides a good insight into the full potential of this unusual device. The only thing that might hurt a bit is the price, but for those of us who really want to explore the full potential of our routers its purchase would be worth it.

▲ The 'push me-pull you' cut action initially seems a little alarming, but holding the work with one hand while moving the router with the other feels OK

Contact: **Everglades International Ltd**, The Old Station, Station Road, Cheddar, Somerset BS27 3AH, Tel: 01934 744051, Fax: 01934 743184 ●

The finished Veritas
router table in action

Tasty table top

TESTER

Anthony
Bailey

Anthony Bailey tries out
the Veritas Router Table Top
and makes a base for it

▲ *Two alloy castings may be
adjusted for clamping on any router*

Veritas have established a reputation
for innovation combined with high
quality engineering and a rather traditional feel to their products, so I
was interested to see just how far this phi-
losophy influences their router table top and
its various accessories.

I was, therefore, pleased to note that
while the rolled steel of the table top may be
basic, it is carefully manufactured to give a
flat, pit-free machining surface.

Construction

Four lengths of studding swaged into the
steel plate fix the top down, and two alloy

castings underneath can be adjusted to
centre and clamp any router.

Fitted to these castings are cast-alloy
hold-downs with springs. With the base
clamps pre-set, removing and refitting your
router quickly and accurately in position is
dead easy.

The hold-downs can be reversed in order to
take either plunge router bases or the fixed
base Stanley/Porter Cable type.

Returning to the top side, the plastic insert
rings supplied are cammed into position by fitting the supplied rollpins to a home-made
wooden disc.

The dovetail profile of the slightly eccentri-

cally-shaped centre hole ensures that the
inserts lock tightly into position, flush with the
table surface. In fact, one insert takes a steel
pin which is fitted in the router collet to accurately centre the router when first setting up.

Two tapped holes for 'fulcrum posts' support a dust shield for profiling with a bear-
ing-guided cutter. A last neat trick is the
provision of four centre-line scorings on all ▶

"A nice touch is the dinky little screwdriver which stows four bits and the hex shaft in its handle"

◀ *The router can be removed and replaced quickly once the clamps are set*

The three-part ally fence shown ▶ here on the bed with the plastic insert rings

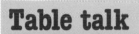

Table talk

To make the base I used up various workshop scraps.

After preparing all the parts, I glued up the two L-shaped upright pieces in two stages, brought them together with glue and left them to dry. The upper and lower frames were glued and screwed using the superb Winzer Würth Ecofast self-tapping screws. Pre-drill the holes first, and then, when the 'Ls' are dry, bring the whole piece together, glue and cramp it on a level surface and leave overnight.

Two bars which fit under the top by fixing onto the studding slip into the top of the frame to hold the top in place. The ends of these bars must be bevelled for an easy fit; the two 'props', which are screwed to the inside of the frame, can then support the top when raised to facilitate cutter changing and speed setting.

Each has a different length of dowel at the end so that the table can be safely propped on one support and then the other.

◀ *The fence clamps firmly to the bed; a micrometer fence adjuster pushes forward when the fence is loose*

edges of the table so that fence setting can be accurately achieved.

Accessories

The three part extruded fence is fastened to the gauge-plate table by clamps on its underside. The lower extrusions can be moved apart to accommodate different cutters; for easy resetting, wood subfences can be fitted.

It comes with a two-part spring hold-down for safe work control. A nice touch is the dinky little screwdriver which stows four bits and the hex shaft in its handle.

An add-on micrometer fence adjuster merely clamps onto the table behind the fence, pushing it forward when the fence is loose.

Other accessories include a perspex cover guard for exposed machining and a perspex guard that fixes to the fence.

The neatest and most efficient item is the extraction port which sits behind the fence. Four powerful magnets hold the port down with a vice like grip — something you can only do with a steel table top of course! The pipe fits into the port and has an optional reducer so that it will fit smaller hoses.

Table

Now for the catch: having got you to spend all that money, Veritas want you to make

▲ A two-part hold-down is included with the table

▲ An accessory perspex cover guard protects against exposed machining

▲ Some of the wooden components that are needed to complete the router table

Facts and figures

Price for Router Table	£139
Manufacturer	Veritas— Ogdensburg N.Y. USA & Ottawa, Canada
Table size	610 x 405 x 5mm (24 x 16 x ³/₁₆in)
Insert size	100mm (4in) diameter
Accessories, prices	Adjustable aluminium fence £129, dust chute and reducer £30, hose and adapter £20, pair of sub fence fine adjusters, pr.£9.25, table safety shield £7.25, fence safety shield £8.50, router table stand £56. (all prices include VAT)
Available from:	BriMarc Associates, 8 Ladbroke Park, Millers Road, Warwick, Warwickshire CV34 5AE, tel 01926 493389, fax 01926 491357

Four powerful magnets hold down the extraction port

your own table!* You have to make a timber base for it, unless mounted in a Workmate or bench top.

The manual gives drawings for an open framework in either softwood or hardwood.

On test

The weight of the rigid steel top holds it so firmly in place that it hardly needs to be fixed down and the fence can easily be adjusted when mounted on it.

Extraction works well and I really like the use of magnets for placement.

On fitting my MOF 177E onto the brackets it was difficult to manipulate the two adjustable, hold-down clamps to hold the router without fouling the body slightly, thus limiting the plunge up through the table; I felt this common enough model

should have snapped into place.

Nevertheless, it works, as do the Veritas table and accessories as a whole.

The real problem is the cost; since you really need all the parts for it to operate at full efficiency it becomes pricey.

*Since writing this test Veritas have introduced a ready-made wooden base costing £56 and including a double-prop system. ●

Two props support the ▶ top when raised to make the job of cutter changing and speed setting easier

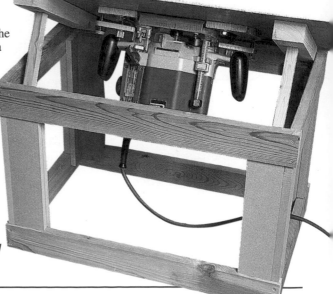

⌐┘PERLES
OF808 ROUTER

SPECIFICATION

850 WATT MOTOR

PLUNGE CUT
CAPACITY 0-50MM

NO-LOAD SPEED
25000RPM

ADJUSTABLE
FENCE PLATES

MICRO ADJUSTER
ON THE GUIDE FENCE

3-STAGE
DEPTH ADJUSTMENT

SPINDLE LOCK

CAN BE FITTED TO
MOST ROUTER TABLES
& JIGS

INCLUDED

8mm CHUCK

1/4" COLLET (U.K. & EIRE)

BEAM TRAMMEL

20mm TEMPLATE

PARALLEL GUIDE

DUST PORT

SPANNER

"**Many of the exterior parts are identical or similar to the recently deleted Elu Mof 96, one of the best routers ever produced**"
The WoodWorker Vol.101 Issue 12

Perles Routers are robustly built and offer superb value for money. Available in Single Speed (Model OF808) and with soft start, variable speed electronics, (Model OF808E)

⌐┘PERLES

FOR
FURTHER
INFORMATION

TEL: **01978 291771**
FAX: **01978 290068**

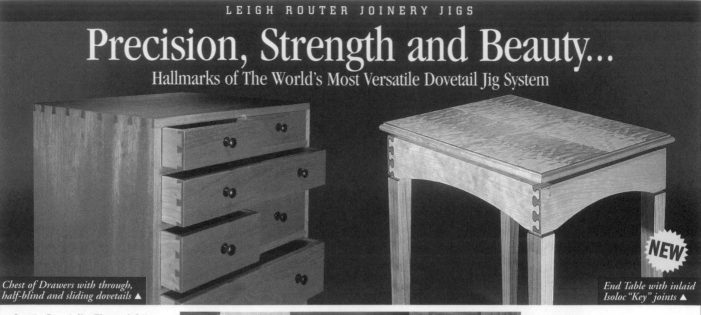

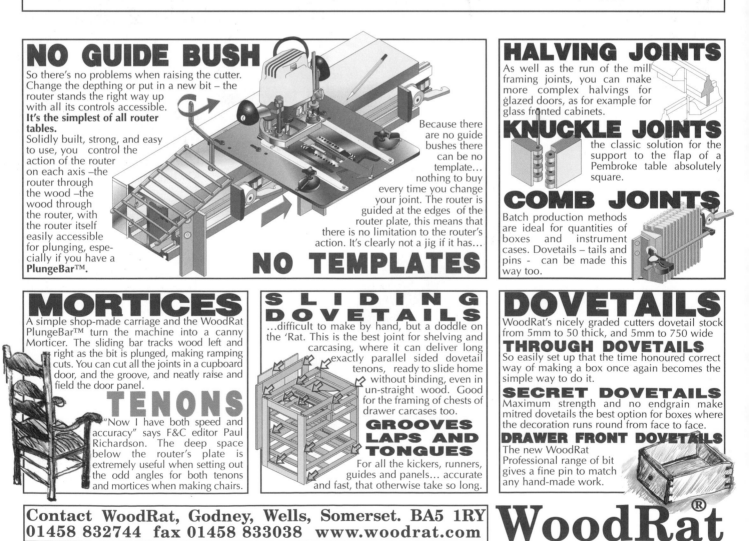

The mighty Woodrat – note the vertical fences attached to the sliding bar. Timber fixed to these is moved left and right by the top-mounted handwheel

£355

Beyond the dovetails

TESTER:
Paul Richardson

Paul Richardson tests a unique router jig, and discovers that dovetails are only the beginning...

THE Woodrat is one of those things that we have all heard of, but unless we've seen one being demonstrated at a show or know someone who has one, we don't really know what they do. I had a vague idea that it was a kind of dovetail jig – it is, but that's not where it ends.

What is it?

So what is it? Well, when a router is mounted on a Woodrat, it can be moved precisely in a fore and aft direction; either at 90° to the body of the jig or at a pre-set angle. The router can also be fixed at any point along this line. When timber is mounted, it can be moved precisely along the body of the jig, or fixed at any point. Simple enough as a principle, but the possibilities it presents are endless.

Almost all jointing operations in wood are carried out in these two planes – in line with and across the timber – and here the plunge action of the router supplies the third dimension. This is because, unlike a machine mounted in an inversion table, the router can be plunged in and out of the timber as freely as if it were hand-held.

Bits that matter

The main body of the Woodrat is a large section aluminium extrusion. This is intended to be hung from a piece of timber fixed to the workshop wall allowing it to be about 375mm (15in) below eye level, but in my workshop I couldn't find a clear area of wall bigger than a postage stamp. Instead I mounted it on the edge of my bench with two clamps, which works but is less suitable in the long term.

A sliding bar is mounted in the front of the main body. This bar moves laterally and ▶

"Unlike a machine mounted in an inversion table, the router can be plunged in and out of the timber as freely as if it were hand-held"

◀ *The router travels fore and aft on a sliding plate. Angles are set with two cams, one each side*

is controlled by a handwheel on the top of the body. Onto the sliding bar are mounted two vertical fences to which the work is clamped by sliding cam locks. This sliding bar assembly gives the left and right dimension.

On top of the body goes a baseplate, and onto the baseplate goes a router plate to which… you guessed it, the router is fixed. This router plate slides forwards and backwards on the baseplate giving the fore and aft dimension.

Jointing principle

Whatever the joint, there will be two mating parts involved. This is why there are two fences fitted to the sliding bar. Once the first part of the joint is cut – mounted against the right hand, cutter position fence – it is re-mounted in the left hand, marker position fence where it acts as a guide for cutting the second part of the joint.

This principle holds true for all interlocking joints like dovetails and finger joints, and also mortices and tenons.

The inventor of the Woodrat, Martin Godfrey, has an enduring enthusiasm for his brainchild. This leads him to produce a regularly updat-

ed owner's handbook containing, amongst other things, advice and details of how to cut 8,000 different joints using the Woodrat. All right, I exaggerate; it's less than 8,000 but still a lot more than I will ever use.

Boring dovetails

Many people will buy this device to cut dovetails, and they won't be disappointed. However, I enjoy cutting dovetails by hand and already have my own tricks for producing them at speed – and these days I don't make so many that the speed of the Woodrat is a great advantage.

If dovetailing for a living, or making a great stack of carcasses or drawers, then it's a different matter.

In the interests of research I made a set of dovetails and pins, and they worked well. I did feel that there was a lot of faffing about involved for just one joint; if I had been making a run of drawers it would have been OK. With a better selection of cutters the result would have looked more attractive; proportions are very important and the cutter I used is a bit brutal.

Woodrat market their own cutters which would have helped. Interestingly they are in HSS rather than tungsten tipped – which means a sharper cutter with a better grind angle for wood – as long as they are not used on abrasive, man-made boards the edge will hold well.

▲ *Work is clamped securely to the vertical fence with strong cam clamps*

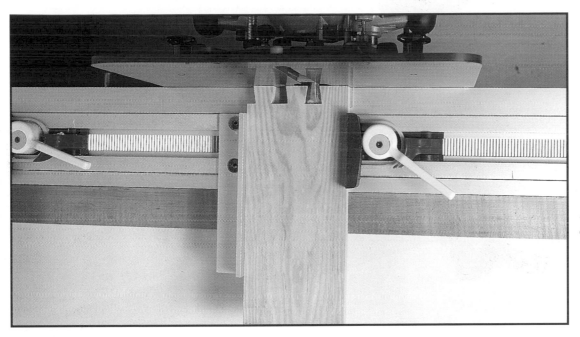

◀ **Dovetails are only the beginning**

Terrific tenons

Having done my dovetail duty, I next tackled a joint that I have been wrestling with for years – the humble tenon.

Mortices are easy. I use a router or a hollow chisel morticer for these, and in either case they are quick to produce in batches. Tenons are another story. I've used every method known to man to cut tenons, and I've never achieved a satisfactory balance between speed and accuracy   until now.

A rail is clamped vertically to the fence, the router is locked along its travel at the thickness of the tenon's shoulder, and the cutter is plunged to the length of the tenon.

Winding the handle on top of the Woodrat causes the stock to travel smoothly across the cutter. Turn the stock round to cut the other faces, and that's it. Straight, square, accurately dimensioned tenons again and again.

Making angled tenons for chair parts is just as easy with a tapered wedge between stock and fence, and haunches, double tenons and so on hardly need thinking about.

Another interesting Woodrat speciality is that it allows the material to be back-fed into the cutter. Normally this would result in Armageddon (as in "Armageddon out of here"), especially trying to cut the

full length of a tenon in a single pass, but the Woodrat's winch-feed makes it an undramatic affair.

The advantage of back-feeding is that there is no breakout – the tenon pictured is straight off the cutter, and is clean enough to be glued up immediately.

Conclusion

For me the Woodrat would pay for itself used solely for tenoning. I would also use it for sliding dovetails, such as are used on shelf ends and tripod-table legs, and as I got used to the way it works I am sure I would find more work for it.

The only limitation is the user's ability to grasp the concept, and here the beginner has the advantage. Because I have preconceived ideas about how to make joints it is harder for me to think in terms of the Woodrat. Someone less set in their ways would be able to exploit more of its features.

Build quality is excellent, after-sales service is good and the owner's manual is comprehensive if erratic. In the hands of an imaginative router user, this is a powerful tool.

■ **Price:** £355 including VAT and delivery.
■ **Available from:** Woodrat, The Old School, Godney, Wells, Somerset BA5 1RY, tel 01458 832744, fax 01458 833038. ●

"I've used every method known to man to cut tenons, and I've never achieved a satisfactory balance between speed and accuracy – until now"

▲ **This perfectly square tenon was cut in seconds – note the shoulders, clean as a whistle straight from the cutter thanks to back-feeding**

Roger Smith

Roger Smith puts the D4 Leigh dovetail jig through its paces

Hand-cut pr

Cutting the tails with the straight fingers outermost

Until now I've always produced dovetail joints by hand, so have become quite adept at the task. But when time is pressing dovetailing can be a repetitive and laborious chore.

Most dovetail jigs lack appeal because they create dovetails of the same spacing apart no matter what the width of the workpiece, and the cutters tend to be large, making the end result look clumsy.

Then I got to work on the Leigh…The dovetails created with their latest incarnation, the D4, look impressive and were nearly slim enough to appear hand-cut; they fit together well and can be spaced to suit the workpiece. Bliss.

Construction

The first impression of the jig is its superb build quality. It has a cast-aluminium chassis and box-steel clamping bars. The assembly which creates the dovetails sits on top of the jig and consists of two chrome-steel bars that a number of cast-aluminium fingers slide on.

The first daunting task is to assemble the many parts onto the chassis; any fears about how to do this are soon put to rest after looking through the excellent manual. It is clearly laid out, easy to follow and features informative diagrams. Also included are sections on general safety advice and useful hints and tips on producing a good joint.

Although the standard jig is easily capable of producing many variations of a dovetail joint including through, half-blind, rabbetted, end-on-end, asymmetric and sliding dovetails, I opted to see how it coped with the simplest and most commonly used through type.

Getting started

The jig must first be set up — a slightly fiddly job that has to be done only once and involves preparing two pieces of wood that have a straight edge and an end square to it.

They are placed vertically and horizontally in the jig and used to set the sidestop bumpers, against which workpieces are butted to ensure accuracy on every subsequent workpiece. Once this is done the dovetailing process can begin.

Place a test workpiece vertically in the jig, inside face out

▼ *Looking down on the assembled jig*

▲ *The guide rail is flipped over to route the pins*

ecision

▼ *The first attempt at a through dovetail joint sits proudly on the Leigh jig*

"The standard jig is easily capable of producing many variations of a dovetail joint"

and edge against the sidestops, and tighten up with the easy-to-use cam-clamps. Then the guide-fingers are spaced apart, tapered ends out, to suit the width of the workpiece; they can be measured but I found positioning them by eye to be pretty accurate.

A supplied guide-bush specific to your router model is then attached to the baseplate and the supplied dovetail cutter installed. The ELU MOF 96 was my second choice, the 10mm collet for my MOF 177 having

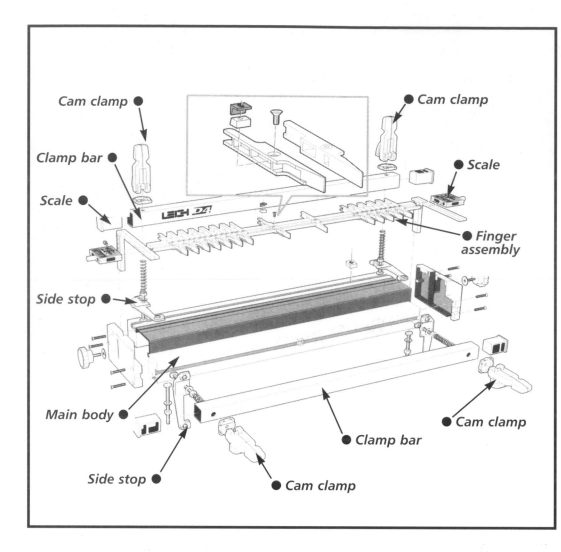

Cam clamp ●

Cam clamp ●

Clamp bar ●

● Scale

Scale ●

● Finger assembly

Side stop ●

Main body ●

● Cam clamp

● Clamp bar

Side stop ●

● Cam clamp

Facts and figures

The basic D4 Leigh dovetail jig costs £360 including VAT. It is available from Leigh Industries (UK) Ltd, PO Box 666, Chippenham, Wiltshire SN15 5QT, tel 01249 750272, fax 01249 758866.
The company also stocks the following accessories: finger-jointing template, mortice and tenoning template, isolock template, guide bushes and cutters.

"After some swotting up in the manual and a little hands-on experience the jig became incredibly easy to set up and use"

disappeared just as it was needed, and the larger router would indeed have been preferable as the 96 tended to groan at the size of cut needed; used carefully, however, it coped.

The guide-bar is then turned over, straight fingers out, and the router placed onto them. Plunge the router so the cutter lines up with a mark previously made by placing a piece of wood of the correct thickness under the guide-fingers.

The tails are then carefully routed, running the guide-bush against the guide-fingers and making sure every part is cut.

To rout the pins, flip over the guide-bar so the tapered fingers face out, and put the next test

piece of wood in the jig, inside face out and against the side-stop bumpers. Install the straight-fluted cutter into the router, set it to depth and carefully rout out the pins.

Now the two parts can be put together to see how well they fit. On my test pieces of wood the joint was pretty good for a first attempt, but a bit tight. After some adjustments were made to the scale settings on the sides of the jig, the test pieces were replaced and a second cut taken.

When tried back together the joint fitted perfectly although there was a little breakout that slightly marred the finish. A quick look at the hints and tips

section in the back of the manual shows how to avoid this.

In use
After some swotting up in the manual and a little hands-on experience the jig became incredibly easy to set up and use.

A careful working procedure must be adopted: mark the inside faces of all components then make sure they are correctly placed in the jig — without thinking I marked the outside faces of the workpieces so had to make sure these were facing in.

As with most wood machining it's a good idea to use test pieces of wood when setting up, so making sure that a perfectly fitting joint is achieved.

Conclusion
The finished joint I created with my first attempt was enough to convince me that the Leigh deserves a place in my workshop.

I like it very much, it is easy to set up and operate, but does require meticulous marking-out — a procedure which is even more necessary when hand-cutting dovetails!

I will probably mostly use the jig for basic through dovetailing on drawer boxes; I'm also keen to try out the many other accessories available, and so increase the range of joints and decorative effects possible. ●

The New Generation of Tungsten Carbide Straight Bits

- Disposable Tungsten Carbide double sided inserts with Kawedur coating for maximum durability.

- No more re-sharpening, ready to use with diameter always correct.

- Suitable for plunge cutting.

- Available in 1/4" and 1/2" Shank sizes as well as standard Metric.

- All Versofix cutters conform to German BG-Test making them suitable for hand Routers.

For full details of our Versofix Router cutters and many other innovative products please ask for a copy of our free Retail Catalogue, or speak to your local KWO stockist.

KWO Tools (UK) Ltd., 4 Strawberry Vale, Vale Road, Tonbridge Kent TN9 1SJ
Tel: 01732 364444 Fax: 01732 351144

ROUTER SPECIFICATIONS

N.B. Prices quoted are the recommended retail prices, inclusive of VAT.
Check dealers for discounted prices.
Contact addresses on pages 116-118.

ATLAS COPCO 0FS 720 (see page 88)
720W. 6.35mm collet supplied. Maximum plunge 50mm (2in). 25,000rpm. Weight 2.5kg. Price £270.

ATLAS COPCO OFSE 2000 (see page 95)
2000W. 8mm, 12mm and $\frac{1}{2}$in collets supplied. Maximum plunge 75mm (3in). 8,000-24,000rpm. Soft start. 240V. Spindle lock and dust extraction. Weight 5.2kg. Price £462.

Contact: ATLAS COPCO TOOLS LTD
(Tel: 01442 61201. Fax: 01442 240596)

BOSCH GOF 900 ACE (see page 90)
900W. $\frac{1}{4}$in collet supplied. Maximum plunge 50mm (2in). 12,000-24,000rpm. Soft start. 240/110V. Spindle lock and dust extraction. Weight 3.5kg. Price £327.

BOSCH GOF 1600 A (see page 84)
1600W. $\frac{1}{4}$in and $\frac{1}{2}$in collets supplied, with option on 6mm, 8mm, $\frac{3}{8}$in and 12mm collets. Maximum plunge 75mm (3in). 25,000rpm. 240/110V. Spindle lock and dust extraction. Weight 5.7kg. Price £398.

Contact: ROBERT BOSCH LTD
(Tel: 01895 834466. Fax: 01895 838388)

DeWALT 613 (see page 90)
800W. $\frac{1}{4}$in collet supplied, option on 6mm and 8mm collet. Maximum plunge 35mm (1$\frac{3}{8}$in). 27,000rpm. 240/110V. Spindle lock and dust extraction. Weight 2.7kg. Price £233.

DeWALT 621 and **ELU** 0F 97EK (see page 89)
1100W. $\frac{1}{4}$in collet supplied, with option on 6mm and 8mm collets. Maximum plunge 55mm (2$\frac{1}{4}$in). 8,000-24,000rpm. Soft start. 240/110V. Spindle lock and dust extraction. Weight 3.3kg. Price £364.

DeWALT 625E (see page 95)
1850W. $\frac{1}{4}$in and $\frac{1}{2}$in collets supplied, with option on 6mm, 8mm and 12mm collets. Maximum plunge 65mm (2$\frac{1}{4}$in). 20,000rpm. 240/110V. Spindle lock and dust extraction. Weight 5.1kg. Price £535.

Contact: BLACK & DECKER POWER TOOLS LTD
(Tel: 01753 511234. Fax: 01753 500843)

ELU OF 97EK - *see* DeWALT 621 (see page 89)

EINHELL EOF 850 SP (see page 92)
850W. $\frac{1}{4}$in and 8mm collets supplied. Maximum plunge 50mm (2in). 24,000rpm. 240V. Dust extraction. Price £152.

Contact: BLADES
(Tel: 01489 885221. Fax: 01489 885221)

FESTO OF 900 E (see page 90)
900W. $\frac{1}{4}$in and 8mm collets supplied, with option on 6mm collet. Maximum plunge 50mm (2in). 10,000-22,000rpm. Soft start. 240V. Spindle lock and dust extraction. Weight 2.7kg. Price £312.

FESTO 0F 2000 E Plus (see page 95)
1800W. 8mm and 12mm collets supplied, with option on 6mm, $\frac{1}{4}$in, $\frac{3}{8}$in and $\frac{1}{2}$in collets. Maximum plunge 65mm (2$\frac{1}{2}$in). 12,000-22,000rpm. Soft start. 240V. Spindle lock and dust extraction. Weight 5.1kg. Price £512.

Contact: MINDEN INDUSTRIAL LTD
(Tel: 01284 760791. Fax: 01284 702156)

FREUD FT2000VCE (see page 83)
1900W. $\frac{1}{4}$in and $\frac{1}{2}$in collets supplied, with option on $\frac{3}{8}$in collet. Maximum plunge 70mm (2$\frac{3}{4}$in); 8,000-22,000rpm; Soft start; 240/110V. Spindle lock and dust extraction. Weight: 6.0kg.Price £340.

Contact: FREUD TOOLING UK LTD
(Tel: 0113 245 3737. Fax: 0113 243 8883)

HITACHI M 8 (see page 91)
800W. $\frac{1}{4}$in collet supplied. Maximum plunge 50mm (2in). 25,000rpm. 240V. Spindle lock. Weight 2.7kg. Price £252.

HITACHI M 8V (see page 92)
800W. $\frac{1}{4}$in collet supplied. Maximum plunge 50mm (2in). 10,000-25,000rpm. Soft start. 240V. Spindle lock. Weight 2.8kg. Price £319.

HITACHI M 12SA (see page 83)
1600W. $\frac{1}{4}$in and $\frac{1}{2}$in collets, with option on $\frac{3}{8}$in collet. Maximum plunge 62mm (2$\frac{3}{8}$in). 22,000rpm. 240V; Spindle lock. Weight: 5.2kg. Price £390.

HITACHI M 12V (see page 94)
1850W. $\frac{1}{4}$in and $\frac{1}{2}$in collets supplied, with option on $\frac{3}{8}$in collet. Maximum plunge 62mm (2$\frac{3}{8}$in). 8,000-20,000rpm. Soft start. 240V. Spindle lock. Weight 5.3kg. Price £457.

Contact: HITACHI POWER TOOLS
(Tel: 01908 291166. Fax: 01908 232868)

MAFELL LO 50E (see page 86)
900W. 8mm collet supplied, with option on 6mm and 1/4in collets. Maximum plunge 50mm (2In); 10,000-22,000rpm; Soft start; 240V; Spindle lock and dust extraction. Weight: 2.7kg. Price £229

MAFELL LO 65E (see page 87)
1800W. 8mm collet supplied, with option on 6mm, 1/4in and 12mm collets. Maximum plunge 65mm
(2 1/2in); 8,000-20,000rpm; Soft start; 240/110V; Spindle lock and dust extraction.
Weight 5.5kg. Price £435.

Contact: NMA AGENCIES
(Tel: 01484 531446. Fax: 01484 432906)

MAKITA 3612BR (see page 84)
1600W. 1/4in, 3/8in and 1/2in collets supplied. Maximum plunge 65mm (2 3/8in). 23,000rpm. 240/110V. Weight 5.7kg. Price £397.

Contact: MAKITA (UK) LTD
(Tel: 01908 211678. Fax: 01908 211400)

METABO OFE 1229 SIGNAL (see page 89)
1200W. 1/4in collet supplied, with option on 6mm and 8mm collets. Maximum plunge 50mm (2in). 27,000rpm. 240/110V. Spindle lock and dust extraction. Weight 3.4kg. Price £448.

METABO OFE 1812 (see page 96)
1800W. 1/2in collet supplied, with option on 6mm, 1/4In, 8mm, 1/2in and 12mm collets. Maximum plunge 80mm (3 1/2in). 8,000-24,000rpm. Soft start. 240/110V. Spindle lock and dust extraction. Weight 5.1kg. Price £601.

Contact: DRAPER TOOLS LTD
(Tel: 01703 266355. Fax: 01703 260784)

RYOBI RE 155 K (see page 88)
800W. 1/4in collet supplied, with option on 8mm collet. Maximum plunge 50mm (2in). 10,000-27,000rpm. Soft start. 240V. Spindle lock and dust extraction. Weight 3.0kg. Price £292.

RYOBI RE 601 (see page 85)
2050W. 6mm, 1/4in, 8mm, 3/8in and 1/2in collets supplied. Maximum plunge 10,000-23,000rpm.
Soft start. 240/110V. Spindle lock and dust extraction. 6.2kg. Price £428.

Contact: RYOBI POWER LTD EQUIPMENT (UK)
(Tel: 01452 724777. Fax: 01452 727400)

SKIL 1875U1 (see page 82)
1400W. 1/4in and 1/2in collets supplied. Maximum plunge 63.5mm (2 3/8in); 8,000-22,000rpm. Soft start; 240V. Weight: 4.5kg. Price £316

Contact: SKIL POWER TOOLS
(Tel: 01895 838743. Fax: 01895 838802)

CONTACT ADDRESSES

THE **AIR** PRESS COMPANY
148 Coombe Road
Salisbury
Wiltshire
SP2 8BL
Tel/Fax: 01722 330224

A.P.T.C.
(see **AXMINSTER** POWER TOOL CENTRE)

ATLAS COPCO TOOLS LTD
PO Box 79
Swallowdale Lane
Hemel Hempstead, Herts
HP2 7HA
Tel: 01442 61202. Fax: 01442 240596

AXMINSTER POWER TOOL CENTRE
Chard Street
Axminster, Devon
EX13 5DZ
Tel: 01297 33656 Fax: 01297 35242

BLACK & DECKER POWER TOOLS LTD
210 Bath Road
Slough, Berkshire
SL1 1YD
Tel: 01753 511234. Fax: 01753 500843

BLADES
271 Botley Road
Burridge, Southampton
SO31 1BS
Tel/Fax: 01489 885221

ROBERT **BOSCH** LTD
PO Box 98, Broadwater Park
North Orbitol Road
Denham, Uxbridge
Middlesex UB9 5HT
Tel: 01895 834466. Fax: 01895 838388

BRIMARC ASSOCIATES
8 Ladbroke Park
Millers Road
Warwick, Warwickshire
CV34 5AE
Tel: 01926 493389 Fax: 01926 491357

DELTA UK
Westwings House
Station Road
Guiseley, West Yorkshire
LS20 8BX
Tel: 01943 873535. Fax: 01943 875959

DeWALT POWER TOOLS LTD
210 Bath Road
Slough, Berkshire
SL1 3YD
Tel: 01753 567055 Fax: 01753 521312

DRAPER TOOLS LTD
Hursley Road
Chandlers Ford
Eastleigh, Hampshire
SO5 5YF
Tel: 01703 266355 Fax: 01703 260784

ELU POWER TOOLS LTD
210 Bath Road
Slough, Berkshire
SL1 3YD
Tel: 01753 576717. Fax: 01753 521312.

EVERGLADES INTERNATIONAL LTD
The Old Station, Station Road
Cheddar, Somerset
BS27 3AH
Tel: 01934 744051 Fax: 01934 743184

FREUD TOOLING UK LTD
Unit 3 Emmanuel
Trading Estate, Springwell Road
Leeds
LS12 1AT
Tel: 0113 245 3737. Fax: 0113 243 8883

HITACHI POWER TOOLS
Precedent Drive
Rooksley
Milton Keynes, Buckinghamshire
MK13 8PJ
Tel: 01908 291166. Fax: 01908 232868

HOFFMANN MACHINE CO LTD
Lane Head
Mewith High Bentham
Nr Lancaster
LA2 7DL
Tel: 01524 262500. Fax: 01524 262220

JKO LTD
Hughenden Avenue
High Wycombe, Bucks.
HP13 5SQ
Tel: 01494 521051. Fax: 01494 461176

JORDAN WOOD MACHINERY LTD
Unit 6B
Philadelphia Complex
Houghton-le-Spring, Tyne & Wear
DH4 4UG
Tel: 0191 5840784. Fax: 0191 5842973

LEIGH INDUSTRIES (UK) LTD
PO Box 666
Chippenham, Wiltshire
SN15 5QT
Tel: 01249 750272 Fax: 01249 758866

MAESTRI-KEAR (UK) LTD
Little Mannings
Winterpit Lane, Mannings Heath
Horsham, West Sussex
RH13 6LZ
Tel: 01403 275575 Fax: 01403 271270

MAKITA (UK) LTD
Michigan Drive
Tongwell
Milton Keynes, Bucks.
MK15 8JD
Tel: 01908 211678. Fax: 01908 211400

MINDEN INDUSTRIAL LTD
16 Greyfriars Road
Moreton Hall
Bury St Edmunds, Suffolk
IP32 7DX
Tel: 01284 760791 Fax: 01284 702156

NEY LTD
Falkland Close
Charter Avenue Industrial Estate
Tile Hill
Coventry
CV4 8UA
Tel: 01203 694794. Fax: 01203 694190

NMA AGENCIES
34 Elmfield Road
Birkby, Huddersfield
West Yorkshire
HD2 2XH
Tel: 01484 531446 Fax: 01484 432906

PRO MACHINE TOOLS LTD
17 Station Road Business Park
Barnack, Stamford
Lincs. PE9 3DW
Tel: 01780 740956. Fax: 01780 740957

REXON LTD
1, The Summit
Barbot Hall Industrial Estate
Maningham Road
Rotherham
S61 4RJ
Tel: 01709 361158. Fax: 01709 821966

RYOBI POWER EQUIPMENT (UK) LTD
Pavilion 1
Olympus Park Business Centre
Quedgeley, Glos.
GL2 6NF
Tel: 01452 724777. Fax: 01452 727400

SCHEPPACH
NMA (Agencies)
34 Elmfield Road
Birkby, Huddersfield
West Yorkshire
HD2 2HX
Tel: 01484 531446 Fax: 01484 432906

SCM GB
Dabell Avenue
Blenheim Industrial Estate
Bulwell, Nottingham
NG8 8WA
Tel: 0115 977 0044. Fax: 0115 977 0946

SCOTT & SERGEANT
1 Blatchford Road
Horsham, West Sussex
RH13 5QZ
Tel: 01403 273000. Fax: 01403 274444

M. **SEDGWICK** & CO LTD
Swinnow Lane
Leeds
LS13 4QG
Tel: 0113 2570637. Fax: 0113 2393412

SKIL POWER TOOLS
PO Box 98, Broadwater Park
North Orbitol Road
Denham, Uxbridge
Middlesex
UB9 5HT
Tel: 01895 838743. Fax: 01895 838802

STAYER POWER TOOLS
Unit 9, Guildford Industrial Estate
Guildford, Surrey
GU2 5YT
Tel: 01483 454502. Fax: 01483 454415

WILSON BROTHERS LTD
Head Office, J3 Springhead Enterprise Park
Springhead Road
Northfleet, Kent
DA11 8HL
Tel: 01474 561414. Fax: 01474 561515

WOODRAT
The Old School
Godney
Wells, Somerset
BA5 1RY
Tel: 01458 832744 Fax: 01458 833038

Titles available from
GMC PUBLICATIONS

BOOKS

WOODWORKING

40 More Woodworking Plans & Projects	*GMC Publications*
Bird Boxes and Feeders for the Garden	*Dave Mackenzie*
Complete Woodfinishing	*Ian Hosker*
Electric Woodwork	*Jeremy Broun*
Furniture & Cabinetmaking Projects	*GMC Publications*
Furniture Projects	*Rod Wales*
Furniture Restoration (Practical Crafts)	*Kevin Jan Bonner*
Furniture Restoration and Repair for Beginners	*Kevin Jan Bonner*
Green Woodwork	*Mike Abbott*
The Incredible Router	*Jeremy Broun*
Making & Modifying Woodworking Tools	*Jim Kingshott*
Making Chairs and Tables	*GMC Publications*
Making Fine Furniture	*Tom Darby*
Making Little Boxes from Wood	*John Bennett*
Making Shaker Furniture	*Barry Jackson*
Pine Furniture Projects for the Home	*Dave Mackenzie*
Sharpening Pocket Reference Book	*Jim Kingshott*
Sharpening: The Complete Guide	*Jim Kingshott*
Space-Saving Furniture Projects	*Dave Mackenzie*
Stickmaking: A Complete Course	*Andrew Jones & Clive George*
Test Reports: *The Router* and *Furniture & Cabinetmaking*	*GMC Publications*
Veneering: A Complete Course	*Ian Hosker*
Woodfinishing Handbook (Practical Crafts)	*Ian Hosker*
Woodworking Plans and Projects	*GMC Publications*
The Workshop	*Jim Kingshott*

WOODTURNING

Adventures in Woodturning	*David Springett*
Bert Marsh: Woodturner	*Bert Marsh*
Bill Jones' Notes from the Turning Shop	*Bill Jones*
Bill Jones' Further Notes from the Turning Shop	*Bill Jones*
Colouring Techniques for Woodturners	*Jan Sanders*
The Craftsman Woodturner	*Peter Child*
Decorative Techniques for Woodturners	*Hilary Bowen*
Essential Tips for Woodturners	*GMC Publications*
Faceplate Turning	*GMC Publications*
Fun at the Lathe	*R.C. Bell*
Illustrated Woodturning Techniques	*John Hunnex*
Intermediate Woodturning Projects	*GMC Publications*
Keith Rowley's Woodturning Projects	*Keith Rowley*
Make Money from Woodturning	*Ann & Bob Phillips*
Multi-Centre Woodturning	*Ray Hopper*
Pleasure and Profit from Woodturning	*Reg Sherwin*
Practical Tips for Turners & Carvers	*GMC Publications*
Practical Tips for Woodturners	*GMC Publications*
Spindle Turning	*GMC Publications*
Turning Miniatures in Wood	*John Sainsbury*
Turning Wooden Toys	*Terry Lawrence*
Understanding Woodturning	*Ann & Bob Phillips*
Useful Techniques for Woodturners	*GMC Publications*
Useful Woodturning Projects	*GMC Publications*
Woodturning: A Foundation Course	*Keith Rowley*
Woodturning: A Source Book of Shapes	*John Hunnex*
Woodturning Jewellery	*Hilary Bowen*
Woodturning Masterclass	*Tony Boase*
Woodturning Techniques	*GMC Publications*
Woodturning Tools & Equipment Test Reports	*GMC Publications*
Woodturning Wizardry	*David Springett*

WOODCARVING

The Art of the Woodcarver	*GMC Publications*
Carving Birds & Beasts	*GMC Publications*
Carving on Turning	*Chris Pye*
Carving Realistic Birds	*David Tippey*
Decorative Woodcarving	*Jeremy Williams*
Essential Tips for Woodcarvers	*GMC Publications*
Essential Woodcarving Techniques	*Dick Onians*
Lettercarving in Wood: A Practical Course	*Chris Pye*
Practical Tips for Turners & Carvers	*GMC Publications*
Relief Carving in Wood: A Practical Introduction	*Chris Pye*
Understanding Woodcarving	*GMC Publications*
Understanding Woodcarving in the Round	*GMC Publications*
Useful Techniques for Woodcarvers	*GMC Publications*
Wildfowl Carving - Volume 1	*Jim Pearce*
Wildfowl Carving - Volume 2	*Jim Pearce*
The Woodcarvers	*GMC Publications*
Woodcarving: A Complete Course	*Ron Butterfield*
Woodcarving: A Foundation Course	*Zoë Gertner*
Woodcarving for Beginners	*GMC Publications*
Woodcarving Tools & Equipment Test Reports	*GMC Publications*
Woodcarving Tools, Materials & Equipment	*Chris Pye*

UPHOLSTERY

Seat Weaving (Practical Crafts)	*Ricky Holdstock*
Upholsterer's Pocket Reference Book	*David James*
Upholstery: A Complete Course	*David James*
Upholstery Restoration	*David James*
Upholstery Techniques & Projects	*David James*

TOYMAKING

Designing & Making Wooden Toys	*Terry Kelly*	Restoring Rocking Horses	*Clive Green & Anthony Dew*
Fun to Make Wooden Toys & Games	*Jeff & Jennie Loader*	Scrollsaw Toy Projects	*Ivor Carlyle*
Making Board, Peg & Dice Games	*Jeff & Jennie Loader*	Wooden Toy Projects	*GMC Publications*
Making Wooden Toys & Games	*Jeff & Jennie Loader*		

DOLLS' HOUSES AND MINIATURES

Architecture for Dolls' Houses	*Joyce Percival*	Making Period Dolls' House Accessories	*Andrea Barham*
Beginners' Guide to the Dolls' House Hobby	*Jean Nisbett*	Making Period Dolls' House Furniture	*Derek & Sheila Rowbottom*
The Complete Dolls' House Book	*Jean Nisbett*	Making Tudor Dolls' Houses	*Derek Rowbottom*
Dolls' House Accessories, Fixtures and Fittings	*Andrea Barham*	Making Unusual Miniatures	*Graham Spalding*
Dolls' House Bathrooms: Lots of Little Loos	*Patricia King*	Making Victorian Dolls' House Furniture	*Patricia King*
Easy to Make Dolls' House Accessories	*Andrea Barham*	Miniature Bobbin Lace	*Roz Snowden*
Make Your Own Dolls' House Furniture	*Maurice Harper*	Miniature Embroidery for the Victorian Dolls' House	*Pamela Warner*
Making Dolls' House Furniture	*Patricia King*	Miniature Needlepoint Carpets	*Janet Granger*
Making Georgian Dolls' Houses	*Derek Rowbottom*	The Secrets of the Dolls' House Makers	*Jean Nisbett*
Making Miniature Oriental Rugs & Carpets	*Meik & Ian McNaughton*		

CRAFTS

American Patchwork Designs in Needlepoint	*Melanie Tacon*	Embroidery Tips & Hints	*Harold Hayes*
A Beginners' Guide to Rubber Stamping	*Brenda Hunt*	An Introduction to Crewel Embroidery	*Mave Glenny*
Celtic Knotwork Designs	*Sheila Sturrock*	Making Character Bears	*Valerie Tyler*
Collage from Seeds, Leaves and Flowers	*Joan Carver*	Making Greetings Cards for Beginners	*Pat Sutherland*
Complete Pyrography	*Stephen Poole*	Making Knitwear Fit	*Pat Ashforth & Steve Plummer*
Creating Knitwear Designs	*Pat Ashforth & Steve Plummer*	Needlepoint: A Foundation Course	*Sandra Hardy*
Creative Embroidery Techniques		Pyrography Handbook (Practical Crafts)	*Stephen Poole*
Using Colour Through Gold	*Daphne J. Ashby & Jackie Woolsey*	Tassel Making for Beginners	*Enid Taylor*
Cross Stitch Kitchen Projects	*Janet Granger*	Tatting Collage	*Lindsay Rogers*
Cross Stitch on Colour	*Sheena Rogers*	Temari: A Traditional Japanese Embroidery Technique	*Margaret Ludlow*

THE HOME

Home Ownership: Buying and Maintaining	*Nicholas Snelling*	Security for the Householder: Fitting Locks and Other Devices	*E. Phillips*

VIDEOS

Drop-in and Pinstuffed Seats	*David James*	Twists and Advanced Turning	*Dennis White*
Stuffover Upholstery	*David James*	Sharpening the Professional Way	*Jim Kingshott*
Elliptical Turning	*David Springett*	Sharpening Turning & Carving Tools	*Jim Kingshott*
Woodturning Wizardry	*David Springett*	Bowl Turning	*John Jordan*
Turning Between Centres: The Basics	*Dennis White*	Hollow Turning	*John Jordan*
Turning Bowls	*Dennis White*	Woodturning: A Foundation Course	*Keith Rowley*
Boxes, Goblets and Screw Threads	*Dennis White*	Carving a Figure: The Female Form	*Ray Gonzalez*
Novelties and Projects	*Dennis White*	The Router: A Beginner's Guide	*Alan Goodsell*
Classic Profiles	*Dennis White*	The Scroll Saw: A Beginner's Guide	*John Burke*

MAGAZINES

**Woodturning • Woodcarving • Furniture & Cabinetmaking • The Router
The Dolls' House Magazine • Creative Crafts for the Home • BusinessMatters**

The above represents a full list of all titles currently published or scheduled to be published.
All are available direct from the Publishers or through bookshops, newsagents and specialist retailers.
To place an order, or to obtain a complete catalogue, contact:
GMC Publications,
166 High Street, Lewes, East Sussex BN7 1XU, United Kingdom Tel: 01273 488005 Fax: 01273 478606
Orders by credit card are accepted